Gothick
CORNWALL

Jennifer Westwood

Shire Publications Ltd

Contents

Printed in Great Britain by C. I. Thomas & Sons (Haverfordwest) Ltd, Press Buildings, Merlins Bridge, Haverfordwest, Dyfed SA61 1XF.

British Library Cataloguing in Publication Data: Westwood, Jennifer. Gothick Cornwall. — (Gothick Guides; No. 3). I. Title. II. Series. 914.23704. ISBN 0-7478-0184-3.

Acknowledgements

Thanks are due to Mrs Angela Evans of Pengersick Castle, Praa Sands, both for her helpfulness on matters of local history and for her hospitality; to Caroline Oates, Assistant Librarian of the Folklore Society; to my research assistant and friend Katie Fischel; and to my son Jonathan Chandler who kept the photographic record of our Cornish journeys.

The photographs are acknowledged as follows: Patience Dizon, pages 8 and 25; Cadbury Lamb, pages 7 (both), 9, 16, 17, 20, 26, 30, 31 (both), 33, 35 (top), 36, 38, 39, 41, 43 (top), 50, 51, 52, 53 (bottom), 56, 57, 58, 62, 63, 65, 66 and 70. The remaining photographs are by the author. The illustrations on pages 6 and 37 are by George Cruikshank from Hunt's *Popular Romances of the West of England*, 1881; the remaining line drawings are by Rachel Lewis, and the map on pages 4-5 is by Robert Dizon. The cover design is based on a painting by Michael J. Taylor entitled 'Overgrown Lodge'.

Introduction

Cornwall is a rugged county and it has bred rugged men — fishermen, sailors, tin miners — and their wives, whose lives are documented among other places in its churchyards. It has also bred rugged legends. The Cornish landscape — the wild moors and wilder seas, the sheer cliffs, the very rocks and stones — have stamped their character on Cornish story-telling, raised to a fine art by the wandering 'droll tellers' who once visited the farms. Important elements in that landscape are the stone monuments of the ancient past — more than twenty stone circles, as well as burial chambers and 'menhirs'.

It is scarcely surprising, then, that Cornwall is exceptionally rich in tales of smugglers and wreckers, mermaids and phantom ships, howling elementals, piskies, spriggans, knockers and above all giants. The titanic scale of its natural features has spelled 'giants' since at least the twelfth century, when Cornwall was famous for them. There has been room for only a few.

Giants lead via the rather nasty St Agnes to Cornwall's ubiquitous saints — the missionaries who came to Cornwall in the Dark Ages from Wales and Ireland, leaving behind their names (St Sampson, St Mawgan, St Ruan) and in many places their holy wells. Like the giants, only a handful of these could be included, and for the most part they are the simpler ones whose atmosphere of sanctity has survived both antiquarianism and tourism.

Cornwall may be in England, but it is as Celtic as Brittany or Wales and shares many of their old traditions of drowned cities and lost lands, and of course Arthur. In 1113, when a party of canons from Laon Cathedral came to Bodmin with the cathedral's famous shrine of the Blessed Virgin, a Cornishman with a withered arm kept vigil before it, in hope of a cure. During the night he fell into argument with one of the canons' men about King Arthur. The Cornishman said he was still alive, the canons' servant scoffed; others were drawn into the debate and a general brawl broke out in the church. The canons' men learned the hard way that the Cornish, like the Bretons and Welsh, believed that Arthur had not died and would one day return. In Cornwall, a belief that Arthur lived on as a bird — the raven or the Cornish chough — lingered at least as late as the eighteenth century.

Because of abiding interest in Arthur, much that passes as 'tradition' in Britain today is no more than educated wishful thinking. Tintagel in particular has suffered from the Arthur industry. This book will lead you a merry dance in search of Arthur, but, it is hoped, bring you in the end to the Arthur of folk belief — not the glamorous king of medieval romance, but the larger than life, undying hero. Like the giants, it is a titanic theme, shaped by this matchless landscape. It will also bring you back again and again to *the* great Arthurian theme of Cornwall, the legend — some say history — of Tristan.

Most of what you read will sound like fiction; much of it is true. It is the quality of Cornwall and the Cornish that the boundary is blurred. See Dozmary at cockshut time and the Hurlers in winter, and you will know what I mean.

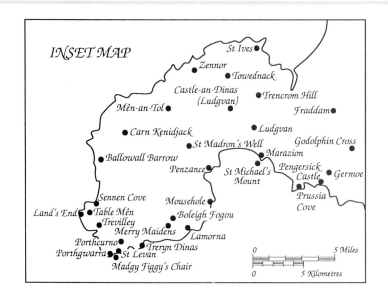

INSET MAP

St Ives
Zennor
Towednack
Castle-an-Dinas
(Ludgvan)
Trencrom Hill
Mên-an-Tol
Fraddam
Carn Kenidjack
Ludgvan
St Madron's Well
Godolphin Cross
Ballowall Barrow
Marazion
Penzance
St Michael's
Mount
Pengersick
Castle
Germoe
Sennen Cove
Prussia
Cove
Mousehole
Land's End
Table Mên
Boleigh Fogou
Trevilley
Merry Maidens
Lamorna
Porthcurno
Treryn Dinas
Porthgwarra
St Levan
Madgy Figgy's Chair

0   5 Miles

0   5 Kilometres

St Mawgan
St Columb
Tre
St Piran's Oratory
St Agnes
Chapel Porth
Ralph's
Cupboard
Godrevy Point
Porthcadjack Cove
Hell's
Mouth
Carn Brea
see INSET MAP
St Ives
Restronguet Creek
Feock
Zennor
Giant's Frying Pan
Di
Fraddam
Penryn
Falmouth
Marazion
Godolphin Cross
Penzance
Breage
Frenchman's Creek
Mousehole
Helston
Helford R
Land's End
The Loe
Mawgan
St Anthony-i
-Meneag
Halliggye
Fogou
Gunwalloe Church Cove
Cury
St Keverne
Mullion
St Ruan's Well
The Rill
Devil's Frying Pan
Pistol Meadow
Landewednack

Gothick
CORNWALL

Places mentioned in the gazetteer

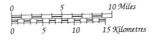

0   5   10 Miles

0   5   10   15 Kilometres

The giant Bolster striding from St Agnes's Beacon to Carn Brea (see page 15).

Using this book

The numbers preceding the directions at the end of each entry are sheet numbers and grid references for Ordnance Survey Landranger maps. In most cases, the 1:50,000 Landranger maps, which can often be borrowed from public libraries, are sufficient. But Cornwall is not a tame county: there are potential hazards, and where larger-scale 1:25,000 OS Pathfinder maps are mentioned, this is not a suggestion but a directive. Wear appropriate footwear; take a torch for fogous.

It is easy to get lost in Cornwall, and directions are consequently often given in considerable detail. For further information on houses open to the public, consult *Historic Houses, Castles and Gardens Open to the Public* (British Leisure Publications, published annually).

The abbreviation AM denotes an officially designated Ancient Monument *not* in the care of English Heritage. The few that are not accessible, or accessible only by prior appointment, are indicated. 'English Heritage' and 'National Trust' for the purposes of this book both imply access. As this may be occasional or seasonal, check their own publications or with the local tourist office.

Place-names in bold type in the text indicate cross-references.

A gazetteer of Gothick places

Altarnun

A Celtic cross by the churchyard gate may date back to the days of the church's traditional founder, St Non, who gave her name to the village ('altar of Non'). Like many Cornish saints, she probably came here as a missionary from Wales in the fifth century, though one legend says she was the beautiful daughter of a Cornish chief. All the tales about her agree that she was the mother of St David, patron saint of Wales, who, according to one fifteenth-century historian, was born at Altarnun.

The carved Vernicle on a bench end at Altarnun.

Carved on a bench end in the church is a fine example of the Vernicle (later known as St Veronica's Handkerchief), the 'true picture' of Christ's face impressed on a cloth, held by an angel.

* * * * *

At the bottom of a field near the vicarage is St Non's Well, which Carew in his *Survey of Cornwall* (1602) describes as a famous 'bowssening' well for lunatics. According to Carew, the water from the well ran into a square walled pool. The mad person was made to stand on the wall and was suddenly pushed backwards into the water. A 'strong fellowe' then dragged him up and down, until the patient was exhausted. If this shock treatment restored his wits, St Non got the credit; otherwise he was 'bowssened' over and over again for as long as he could survive it.

The Celtic cross in the churchyard at Altarnun.

7

Not surprisingly, this 'cure' fell into disuse and the well with it. By the end of the nineteenth century the spring feeding the well had failed because of nearby land drainage, and the well-head itself was broken and overgrown.

OS 201: SX 2281. 7 miles (11 km) west of Launceston, just off A30 to Bodmin.

Ballowall Barrow

Ballowall Barrow, also known as Carn Gloose, stands dramatically on a cliff's edge looking towards Land's End. Built in the bronze age to an unusual plan, it was thought by its excavator to be possibly not a tomb but a symbolic entrance to the Underworld.

Later it was locally believed to be a haunt of fairies: miners on their way home from the Ballowall Mine at night had seen lights there and fairies dancing. The Ballowall Mine itself was a famous place for knockers, the fairy miners who inhabited Cornish tin mines and took their name from the sounds of their working. The knockers only worked good lodes, and miners considered it a sign of good luck whenever they heard them, though they were dangerous if crossed. They were thought to be the remnants of a race who inhabited Cornwall before the coming of Christianity and were neither good enough for Heaven nor bad enough for Hell.

OS 203: SW 355313. Near St Just, 4 miles (6 km) north of Land's End on B3306. From St Just a lane leads west to Cape Cornwall. Carn Gloose Road branches off it to the left and leads to Carn Gloose in under a mile. Ballowall Barrow is left of the lane. English Heritage. Relics of Ballowall Mine, SW 363333 area. Pathfinder 1364: St Ives & Penzance (North).

Bodmin

Perhaps the most extraordinary event to happen at Bodmin is something that befell Robert, Earl of Moreton, a close friend of William

Ballowall Barrow, once believed to be the haunt of fairies.

Bodmin Gaol.

remark in Cornwall, when anyone was sloppily dressed, that he or she would be 'presented in Halagaver Court'. Charles I is said to have once ridden there to view the proceedings.

In Bodmin itself a grimmer justice was meted out. Notorious in fact and fiction, Bodmin Gaol is now a pub and the public can see the gloomy cells of this eighteenth-century prison and such relics of 'correction' as stocks and a pillory.

OS 200, 201: SX 0767. 26 miles (42 km) west of Plymouth. Halagaver Moor, SX 076654 area, west of B3268 from Bodmin to Lostwithiel. A public footpath skirts it, leading right off B3268 roughly opposite Little Halgavor Farm. Use OS Pathfinder 1347 (SX 06/16). Bodmin Gaol is in Berrycombe Road.

Rufus (William II). One day in 1100, when he was hunting in the woods, he became separated from his huntsmen. Riding on to the moor for a clearer view, he was surprised to see a huge black goat approaching. As it drew near, he saw that on its back it carried 'King Rufus', naked and wounded in the breast. Robert commanded the goat in God's name to tell him what he bore and the goat replied: 'I am carrying your king to judgement'. Then it vanished. When Robert met his followers he told them his adventure, and soon after they heard the news that William Rufus had been slain by an arrow in the New Forest.

* * * * *

Bodmin was once famous for a festival known as Bodmin Riding, which used to take place on nearby Halagaver (now Halgavor) Moor. A mock mayor was elected, before whom people were tried for any kind of slovenliness. Sentence was passed and a 'punishment' given. This gave rise to a common

Bodrugan's Leap

From this headland, Sir Henry Trenowth of Bodrugan, a supporter of the House of York during the Wars of the Roses, evaded his Lancastrian enemies, Sir Richard Edgcumbe and William Trevanion, by jumping into the sea and escaping by boat to France. As he leapt from the precipice, Bodrugan bequeathed, with a curse, 'his extravagance to the Trevanions and his folly to the Edgecombes'.

OS 204: SX 0144. 1½ miles (2.5 km) south of Mevagissey via B3273, just south of Chapel Point. National Trust. By footpath only from Portmellon or Gorran Haven.

Boleigh Fogou

Though archaeologists say that the mysterious stone-built underground structures known in Cornwall as 'fogous' (caves) were probably cold storage chambers rather than refuges, one at least has been used as a hiding place in historical times. So large and perfect was Boleigh Fogou in the parish of St Buryan at the time of the Civil

9

years earlier and seduced his wife. Lovelis cursed him aloud and the coven turned on him. When he at length emerged from the cave, he was found by friends singing wildly, having been driven completely insane. He and his hounds are still supposed to haunt the neighbourhood.

OS 203: SW 439252. South-east of St Buryan, 4 miles (7 km) east of Land's End on B3315 from Land's End to Newlyn. The fogou, shown on OS Pathfinder 1368 (SW 32/42), is in private grounds. AM. The best fogou to visit is **Halliggye Fogou.**

Botusfleming

In Botusfleming, across the road from the church and surrounded by iron railings, is a pyramidal tomb. It marks the grave of William Martyn, who died in 1762 and chose to be buried here, so the inscription says, because he had 'no superstitious veneration for church or churchyard'.

OS 201: SX 4061. 2 miles (3 km) north-west of Saltash off A388 from Saltash to Launceston.

Breage

The fifteenth-century granite church of St Breaca contains splendid wall paintings that include, to the right of the door, a gruesome 'Warning to Sabbath Breakers'. This shows Christ's body peppered with wounds from the tools of various trades, symbolising the effect of breaking the Third Commandment and working on a Sunday.

Although St Christopher, patron saint of travellers, is depicted on the other side of the doorway, with a mermaid in the waves at his feet, Breage was no safe haven for seafarers. Many tales are told in Cornwall of wreckers: although in law all wrecks were claimed by the Crown, people living along the coast regarded it as *their* right to salvage any wreck that came their way. They are also accused of show-

War that Cavaliers were hidden there, fed by Mr Levellis (Lovel) of nearby Trewoofe, until they had the opportunity to return to the King's army.

Part of Boleigh Fogou's mystery in the nineteenth century lay in the fact that its full extent was unknown, as a pool of water some distance from the entrance prevented its being explored. Because no one could say otherwise, it was generally believed to end under the parlour of a house in Trove, all that remained of Trewoofe, once the manor house of the Levellis, Lovelis or Lovel family. In fact the fogou is about 40 feet (12 metres) long.

This mistaken notion of its size led to a tradition that witches were in the habit of holding their sabbaths in the 'Fogou Hole' and meeting the Devil there: he had often been heard piping while they danced. A sinister local tale was that Squire Lovelis of Trewoofe, when out hunting, chased a hare into the 'Fugoe Hole'. He came to a broad pool of water and on the other side, gathered round a fire, were scores of the notorious **St Levan** witches (witches were supposed to be able to turn into hares and vice versa).

Presently the witches began dancing round the fire with the leader of their coven, a 'Black Man' (or demon) whom Squire Lovelis recognised as the dark stranger who had come to Trewoofe

ing false lights from clifftops to lure ships on to the rocks and of murdering survivors.

Though the cold-blooded murder of shipwreck victims is commoner in fiction than it was in real life, the people of Breage and other villages around Mount's Bay were feared for wrecking. As it says in a rhyme:

> God keep us from rocks and shelving sands
> And save us from Breage and Germoe men's hands.

OS 203: SW 6128. 3 miles (4 km) west of Helston on A394 to Penzance.

Carn Brea

From a landscape of abandoned mine workings rears the primitive bulk of Carn Brea, crowned with great natural granite boulders and successive works of antiquity. Over and over again this great eminence has been used as a settlement and safe refuge. On its eastern end stands a small medieval castle, part of which is built on very ancient foundations and seems to grow from

The 'Warning to Sabbath Breakers' wall painting at Breage, depicting Christ wounded by the tools of those who work on Sunday.

Carn Brea and the small medieval castle which stands on its eastern end.

the rock. The summit is enclosed by a huge iron age hillfort, and near the top is a massive drystone wall from the neolithic period.

The whole landscape is archaic, especially by fading light, and the diminutive castle perched on the rocks adds a touch of fantasy. No wonder that country people told marvellous tales of this place, among them that it was the scene of a combat between Satan and a troop of saints, during which he was tumbled from the heights, the rocky boulders strewing the Carn being the huge missiles the saints hurled after him.

Another tale of Carn Brea is that a giant called John of Gaunt is buried beneath it. At the western end of the Carn stands a monument erected in 1836 to Francis, Lord de Dunstanville and Basset. Not far from this, a large block of granite with five nearly equal indentations used to be pointed out as the giant's hand, which, poking up through the surface, had been turned to stone.

Carne Beacon.

OS 203: SW 685408. 2 miles (3 km) east of Camborne, south of A30, via A393, then B3297, out of Redruth. A minor road west off B3297 leads through Carnkie. As it is about to leave the village, another road branches off it north, signposted to Carn Brea Castle. This road presently forks, the left fork leading to the castle. The road continues as a track, passable by motor vehicles, up to the medieval castle (now a restaurant). The Giant's Hand is reached by following the path from the castle to the Basset monument and continuing past it towards the brow of the hill. The Hand is on the left.

Carne Beacon

Overlooking Gerrans Bay stands Carne Beacon, an ancient burial mound. At 370 feet (113 metres) in circumference one of the largest round barrows in Britain, it used to be known simply as the Carne. An old tradition says that in it lies Gerennius, king of Cornwall, and buried with him is a golden boat with silver oars. John

12

Whitaker in his *Ancient Cathedral of Cornwall* (1804) surmised that, when Gerennius died, he was brought from his castle of **Dingerein** and ferried with great pomp across Gerrans Bay in a barge plated with gold, a memory of which lingered to Whitaker's own day.

However that may be, so deeply stamped on people's imaginations was the old tale that, when a rumour was put about that Whitaker intended to excavate the barrow, the local farm servants asked their masters for a holiday, to see the buried boat unearthed. Unfortunately for tradition, when the Carne was opened in 1855, only a stone cist containing ashes was found.

Gerennius may be the same person as St Gerent or Gerontius, to whom the church at Gerrans is dedicated. Other possibilities include the historical Geraint, king of Dumnonia (Devon) in the seventh century. Was either of these our Gerennius? Only one thing is certain: the Carne is a noble and imposing mound, a fitting place for a royal burial.

OS 204: SW 913387. About a mile (2 km) south of Veryan, 7 miles (11 km) south-west of Mevagissey and west of A3078 to St Mawes. At a sharp angle in the lane from the hamlet of Carne (SW 913383) to Carne Beach and Gwendra (SW 903384), just before a lane to Veryan leading off to the right, stone steps in the bank mount to a stone stile. This gives on to a footpath, signposted to Churchtown Farm, which leads past Carne Beacon. The Carne, on land owned by the National Trust, is fenced, but a gate gives access. AM. See also **Tregagle's Hole**.

Carn Kenidjack

Not far from St Just stands a natural bastion of stone known as Carn Kenidzhek (now Kenidjack), the 'Hooting Cairn', so called from the wind that whistles amongst its crags. In its shadow are many memorials of the dead — mounds, barrows, standing stones — and into the nineteenth cen-

tury it was feared as a haunt of the Devil, who was reputed to hunt lost souls over the surrounding wasteland.

Two miners coming home one night heard the wild hooting sound that gave the Carn its name, though there was no wind. There was no moon either, yet a strange light played on the Carn and the miners thought they glimpsed gigantic forms passing to and fro. Overtaken by a dark rider robed and hooded in black, they were invited 'Up to the cairn to see the wrastling'. Mysteriously compelled to follow, they found themselves at a gathering of savage-looking men of great size and strength.

Gradually the miners realised that the rider was Old Nick and that what they were witnessing was a wrestling match between demons. When a wrestler was thrown and appeared to be dying, one of the miners forgot this fact and said a prayer over him. At once the rocks trembled as in an earthquake, everything became pitch dark, and there was a great noise of rushing to and fro. The miners were, owing to supernatural interference, unable to find their way and had to spend the night under the Carn, praying that daylight would release them from the spell.

OS 203: SW 387329. Near St Just, 4 miles (6 km) north of Land's End on B3306. East of St Just, B3318 leads north off A3071 (Penzance road) towards Pendeen. A minor road breaks left to Trewellard. A public footpath leads south off this towards Carn Kenidjack after a few yards. Use Pathfinder 1364: St Ives & Penzance (North).

Castle-an-Dinas, Ludgvan

The name of this hillfort, like those of **Treryn Dinas** at Treen and Caer Dane near Perranzabuloe, means roughly 'Danes' castle'. Though these forts and cliff castles are prehistoric, or more often iron age, Cornishmen traditionally said they were built by the Danes.

The Danes were also said to have landed at several places round the coast and founded settlements. Their descendants could be known by their red hair. Red-haired people were generally looked down on, and a common expression of contempt was 'Oh, he [or she] is a red-haired Daäne.' In Sennen Cove there was long a colony of red-haired people, some of whom were still alive in the 1870s, with whom other inhabitants of the district refused to marry.

OS 203: SW 485350. North-west of Ludgvan, 2 miles (4 km) north-east of Penzance, via B3311 (Penzance-St Ives road). Opposite the turn-off on to B3309 to Ludgvan, there is a public bridleway to the Castle. A public footpath runs past Caer Dane, just east of Perranzabuloe, OS 204: SW 778522, beginning a little more than half way along the minor road from Perranzabuloe to Ventongimps. Both AM.

Castle-an-Dinas, St Columb Major

Besides sharing a name with **Castle-an-Dinas**, Ludgvan, this ancient hillfort on Castle Downs was also known among local people as 'Arthur's Hunting Seat'. It was here that Arthur stayed when he hunted on **Goss Moor**. It is also connected with the star-crossed lovers Tristan and Iseult (see **Castle Dore** and **Drustan Stone**). In one version of their story, Iseult's maid Brangwyn betrays Tristan to King Mark, who comes upon him singing to Iseult and wounds him with a poisoned spear. Tristan flees and takes refuge with his friend Dinas of Lidon at his castle, Castle-an-Dinas. There he dies. Tristan's dying in Cornwall would square better with the existence of the **Drustan Stone**, possibly his gravemarker, near Fowey, than his dying in Brittany as he does in the best-known form of the legend.

OS 200: SW 945624. East of St Columb Major, 6 miles (10 km) east of Newquay, on A3059 at its junction with A39. By minor road off this roundabout junction towards Belowda. A public footpath leads north off this road straight up to the fort. AM.

Castle Dore

Though the earthen ramparts of this circular iron age hillfort still survive to 7 feet (2 metres) high and it has a wide view over the surrounding country, other Cornish hillforts and cliff castles are more impressive.

But Castle Dore has the magic of romance. For centuries people have believed that it was once the court of King Mark of Cornwall and scene of the love story of Tristan and Iseult. Best known today from Wagner's opera *Tristan und Isolde*, this ancient tale relates how Tristan, King Mark's nephew, is sent to Ireland to fetch his uncle's new bride, the beautiful Princess Iseult. Aboard the homecoming ship, however, he drinks a magic love potion and falls in love with her, with tragic consequences (see **Drustan Stone**).

Although the original Tristan was probably a Pictish prince in Lowland Scotland, the tale was long ago given a Cornish setting. A twelfth-century poet says King Mark's palace was at 'Lancien', echoed in the name of Lantyan or Lantyne, now a farm. As the medieval manor of Lantyan-in-Golant included Castle Dore, by 'Lancien' he may have meant Castle Dore itself.

Excavation of Castle Dore carried out in 1935-6 suggested that, as the Tristan legend implies, it was occupied in the 'Arthurian period', the sixth century AD. Constructed in about the third century BC and abandoned with the coming of the Romans, it was later given a new lease of life as the formidable stronghold of a Dark Age chieftain. Many archaeologists identify this chieftain with the sixth-century

Castle Dore, believed once to have been the court of King Mark of Cornwall.

Cornish ruler Cynfawr. If, as some people believe, Mark and Cynfawr were the same man, then by the evidence of the **Drustan Stone**, Tristan was his son and not his nephew as in the Arthurian version.

OS 200: SX 103548. West of Golant, 2 miles (3 km) north of Fowey. Castle Dore is on the east (right) side of B3269 from Fowey to Bodmin. Opposite a turn to Tywardreath on the left, a house on the right marked 'Castle Dore' is followed by a parking place. Further down the road, a field gate gives access.

Chapel Porth

The cove of Chapel Porth took its name from a little Gothic chapel that existed until around the end of the eighteenth century and sheltered St Agnes's Well. Country people knew the well as 'Giant's Well', after a giant who once lived in the neighbourhood. His name was Bolster, and he was so huge that he could stand with one foot on **Carn Brea** and the other on St Agnes's Beacon, 6 miles (10 km) apart as the crow flies. One day, when he was striding between the two, he stooped to drink out of 'Giant's Well', leaving the marks of his thumbs imprinted on one of its stones.

Bolster fell in love with St Agnes, a beautiful missionary, and used to follow her around. At last she got rid of him by telling him that he must prove his love by filling a hole in the cliff at Chapel Porth with his blood. Thinking it was only small, Bolster stretched his arm over it and opened a vein with a knife. But the hole opened into the sea, and after pouring his lifeblood into it for several hours he collapsed and died.

The hole remains to prove the story true and red stains on the rocks show where Bolster's blood ran down. He is still commemorated by the Bolster, now known as Bolster Bank, a linear earthwork at the foot of the Beacon. Whether he built it or lies buried under it is an open question.

OS 203: SW 696496. Near St Agnes, 6 miles (9 km) north of Redruth. A minor

15

road from St Agnes leads past St Agnes Beacon to Chapel Porth. National Trust. Bolster Bank (AM), SW 715497.

The Cheesewring

William Camden explained the curious name of this natural phenomenon on Bodmin Moor in his *Britannia* (1610): 'there is a number of good big rockes heaped up together, & under them, one Stone of lesser size, fashioned naturally in forme of a cheese, so as it seemeth to be pressed like a cheese, whereupon it is named Wring-cheese'.

The Cheesewring later became associated with a local stonecutter, Daniel Gumb, whose work can be seen in Linkinhorne churchyard. Although his parents were uneducated, he himself was a great reader with a passion for mathematics and astronomy. Marrying a local girl, he made his home with her in a cave he hollowed out near the Cheesewring. It was big enough to take him and the many children they

The Cheesewring.

produced if they rolled sideways to enter it. He baptised the children himself on prehistoric 'altars' nearby, and neither he nor his family abandoned the cave as long as they lived. Until the cave collapsed, the inscription 'D. Gumb 1735' could be seen above the entrance.

OS 200: SX 258725. Near Minions, 4 miles (7 km) north of Liskeard, off B3254 to Launceston. A track to the Cheesewring is signposted from the north end of Minions, or it can be reached by starting from the Hurlers.

Cotehele

'Ancient, large, strong and faire' was how Carew in his *Survey of Cornwall* (1602) described Cotehele, on the banks of the Tamar, a late medieval house and for centuries the home of the Edgcumbe family, who largely rebuilt it between 1485 and 1627.

In the early nineteenth century it was said that nine hundred years had passed since its foundation and that it possessed an indelible bloodstain, left when a warder of the drawbridge was killed by the lord of the manor on suspicion of treachery. Only on wet days was it visible.

In the woods at Cotehele is a little chapel, said to have been built in the late fifteenth century by Richard Edgcumbe, a supporter of Henry, Earl of Richmond, afterwards King Henry VII. Edgcumbe was once so hotly pursued by the supporters of Richard III that he was forced to hide in the woods at Cotehele. He saved himself by putting a stone in his hat and throwing it into the river. Hearing the splash, his pursuers looked down and, seeing the hat, thought he had jumped into the Tamar and been drowned. When they gave up looking for him, he escaped to Brittany.

Edgcumbe joined the standard of Henry of Richmond once more and returned with him to defeat Richard III at Bosworth Field. For this, he was

Cotehele, the home of the Edgcumbe family.

knighted on the battlefield. To commemorate his deliverance, he built the little chapel on the spot where he had lurked in Cotehele woods.

Though the Edgcumbes virtually ceased to live at Cotehele at the end of the seventeenth century, it was there that another dramatic incident in their family history is said to have taken place. Lady Edgcumbe had died and, about a week after her death, her body had been placed in the family vault. Shortly after, the parish sexton went down into the vault and tried to steal a gold ring off her finger. The ring was tight, and he was pinching the finger to get it off, when the body stirred in its coffin. Horrified, he ran off, leaving his lantern behind. Lady Edgcumbe arose from her coffin and, taking the lantern, made her way to the house. This supposedly happened to the mother of the Sir Richard Edgcumbe created Baron of Mount Edgcumbe in 1748, about five years before he was born, but the same tale of suspended animation is told of other titled ladies in other places.

OS 201: SX 423686. Near St Dominick, 3 miles (5 km) south-east of Callington, east of A388 from Callington to Saltash. Signposted. National Trust.

Cury

An old man from Cury was walking in a cove near Lizard Point when he found a stranded mermaid sitting on a rock. She asked him to help her back to the sea, as her family would be worried, and the old man lifted her piggyback to the water's edge. The grateful mermaid granted him a wish, and he wished for the power to help his neighbours. The mermaid said he must meet her again at a certain half-tide rock to receive instruction. She also gave him her comb, telling him he had only to comb the waves and she would come.

She duly appeared at the half-tide rock — in the nineteenth century still known as Mermaid's Rock — and taught him how to charm disease, break spells and find stolen goods. His descendants inherited his gift, telling this story to account for it. As proof

that it was true, they would produce the mermaid's comb. Sceptics claim it was only a shark's jaw; that a mermaid might well use this for a comb seems not to have occurred to them! Many think this happened at Poldhu Cove.

* * * * *

Brandy for the Parson,
'Baccy for the Clerk

runs the chorus of 'A Smuggler's Song' by Rudyard Kipling (1906). It reflects the fact that in the eighteenth century people of all walks of life were prepared to trade with the smugglers. Parson Woodford, of Weston Longville in Norfolk, was certainly one man of the cloth who saw no harm in evading customs and excise duty when opportunity offered, or in recording in his *Diary of a Country Parson* the visits of the local smuggler to his door.

Another case in real life is that of the parson of Cury, the Reverend Thomas Whitford. A ship, the *Lady Lucy*, coming from Bordeaux with a cargo of wine, brandy, indigo, and coffee berries, was wrecked at **Gunwalloe** early in the morning of 14th December 1739. As it was several hours before daylight, local wreckers seized their chance to plunder the ship before the customs officers arrived. They managed to remove a quantity of wine, and, later, officers searching for the stolen goods discovered four casks of the missing

wine in Whitford's house.

Perhaps there is some truth in the apocryphal story of a parson who, when his service was disturbed by news of a wreck in the neighbourhood, asked the congregation to remain in their seats until he had removed his cassock, 'so that we can all start fair'!

OS 203: SW 6721. 4 miles (6 km) south of Helston, by minor road off A3083 to the Lizard. Poldhu Cove, National Trust.

Devil's Frying Pan

Just south of Cadgwith, a few miles from the tip of the Lizard Peninsula, is the Devil's Frying Pan, once a huge sea cave. The roof has almost entirely collapsed, leaving a natural bridge under which the sea roars through a narrow entry into a roughly circular pool. Dramatic coastal features are often connected with the Devil — there is a **Hell's Mouth** at Portreath.

The Devil's Frying Pan.

OS 204: SW 7214. *At Cadgwith, 3 miles (5 km) north-east of Lizard Point via A3083 and minor road south-east through Grade. Public footpath signposted at beginning of village to 'South Coast Route (Frying Pan)'. National Trust car park beyond gate marked 'Devil's Frying Pan', and gate of Town Place.*

Dingerein Castle

This is the legendary fortress of King Gerennius, buried under **Carne Beacon**. Dingerein today gives little sign of a distinguished past: it shows as a crescent of bank inside a hedge and is partly overgrown.

In the sixteenth century two underground passages connected with it could still be seen. By 1804 the first had disappeared, but the second survived, running down to the sea. Some way inland, the roof had caved in, so it could not be explored. However, it still opened in the face of the cliff in what was locally known as the Mermaid's Hole, being low enough down for a mermaid to have floated in at the top of the tide.

OS 204: SW 882376. *Just beyond Trewithian, 4 miles (6 km) north-east of St Mawes, in the angle between A3078 and the minor road through Curgurrell and Rosevine to Porthcurnick Beach.*

Dodman Point

On Dodman Point there is a well-preserved iron age promontory fort. Once known as *Thica Vosa* or the Hack and Cast, it was said to be the work of a giant, who built it in one night. He was the terror of the neighbourhood until he was despatched by the Gorran doctor by the method St Agnes used at **Chapel Porth**. Once the giant was weak from loss of blood, the doctor kicked him over the cliff, whence it got the name of 'Dodman', or 'Dead Man'.

According to a local rhyme, the wizard Merlin prophesied:

When the Rame Head and Dodman meet
Man and woman will have cause to greet [cry].

The prophecy has yet to be fulfilled — the two headlands are 40 miles (64 km) apart — though some claim it happened when Sir Piers Edgcumbe bought both promontories.

OS 204: SX 0039. *4 miles (6 km) south of Mevagissey by minor road through Portmellon and Trewollock, skirting north round Gorran Haven and turning south to Penare (signposted) shortly after Gorran Churchtown. Parking at Penare. A footpath leads straight up on to the Dodman, with branches left and right skirting the fort, SX 999398/004399. AM.*

Dozmary Pool

Since at least the sixteenth century this small lake on Bodmin Moor has had an eerie reputation. Like many pools, it was thought to be bottomless, but though this was long ago proved untrue — it is very shallow — this did not dispel its mystery and it became associated with Cornwall's most troublesome ghost, Jan or John Tregeagle.

Tregeagle, who in real life was the magistrate who tried to starve Anne Jeffries of **St Teath**, left a bad reputation when he died in 1655. He was said to have seized a child's estate after murdering its parents. When he himself died and was buried at St Breock, he was summoned back from the grave by being named in court at Bodmin. A debtor trying to avoid repaying a loan witnessed by Tregeagle remarked: 'If Tregeagle ever saw it, I wish to God he would come and declare it!' In a flash of lightning, the ghost of Tregeagle appeared, declaring that it would not be so easy to get rid of him as it had been to summon him.

The parsons of Bodmin, however, bound him to the everlasting task of emptying Dozmary Pool with a limpet shell. The shell had holes in it, and the water ran out as fast as he baled. For years he was kept hard at work by a

Dozmary Pool.

pack of demonic hounds, but one night when a storm was raging he raced across the moor to **Roche Rock**. He tried to squeeze in through the east window of St Michael's Chapel but could get only his head in. His howls of fury and despair alerted the priest, who led him to **Padstow**, where he was set to weaving ropes of sand.

His work was washed away with every high tide and this too set him howling. When the people of Padstow could stand no more, they called on St Petroc, who drove him to Bareppa and set him to clearing the beach. He had to carry the sand in sacks to Porthleven and one day as he crossed the estuary he dropped his sack. The sand spilled out, forming the sandbank of Loe Bar and creating the lake behind it known as the Loe.

Furious at losing their harbour, the Porthleven people got their priest to send him to Land's End, where he was set to sweeping the sand from Porthcurno Cove into Mill Bay. At this task he still labours, and the crying of the storm on Bodmin Moor and **Goss Moor**, and along Cornwall's rocky coast, is traditionally explained as Tregeagle roaring.

*OS 201: SX 1974. On Bodmin Moor, west of minor road between Bolventor and St Cleer. Signposted from **Jamaica Inn**, 1¹/₂ miles (2 km). Twilight and winter are the most atmospheric times for this site. Padstow (SW 9175), Bareppa (SW 7829), Porthleven (SW 6225), Porthcurno Cove (SW 3822), Mill Bay (SW 3523).*

Drustan Stone

This 7 foot (2 metre) monolith, thought to have been erected around AD 550, is one of the great Arthurian mysteries. On its north side is a raised T, an early form of the Christian cross, and on the south side in faint lettering is the Latin inscription: DRVSTANS HIC IACIT CVNOWORI FILIUS ('Here lies Drustanus, son of Cunomorus'). It evidently commemorates a dead prince or chieftain. 'Cunomorus' was probably the sixth-century King Cynfawr, but 'Drustanus' is the same name as Tristan.

The stone, which may once have been taller, was moved to its present site only in 1971. Originally it stood nearer the iron age fort of **Castle Dore**, early identified as the court of King Mark of Cornwall, uncle of the legendary

Tristan. Did this mark Tristan's grave?

According to the main form of the legend, Tristan dies not in Cornwall but in Brittany. The story goes that, after three years the power of the magic potion he has drunk begins to fade and, pursued by King Mark's men, he flees to France. There he marries another Iseult, Iseult of the White Hands, daughter of the Duke of Hoel, the ruler of Brittany. But when King Mark puts a price on his head, Tristan returns to Cornwall disguised as a madman to tell his own story. Recognised and innocently betrayed by the dog he has given Iseult, he is re-united with her briefly before being forced to flee, mortally wounded.

Back in Brittany, he sends to Cornwall for Iseult in the belief that only she can heal him. If his messenger succeeds in his mission, he is to return with white sails on his ship; if he fails, the sails are to be black. Iseult sets out at once for Brittany but, as the ship comes in sight, Iseult of the White Hands deceives Tristan into thinking the sails are black. In despair, he dies. Finding her lover dead, Iseult, too, dies of grief and the tragic pair are buried side by side.

From Iseult's grave springs a rose, and from Tristan's a vine, and the two eventually meet and intertwine.

So says the most popular love story of the Middle Ages. But did Mark, perhaps in remorse, bring Tristan's body home? Or did Tristan, as some say, die at the hillfort of **Castle-an-Dinas, St Columb**?

OS 200: SX 112522. Beside A3082 leading down into Fowey from Par. AM.

Falmouth

About halfway across the mouth of Falmouth Harbour, between St Anthony Head and Pendennis Point, is the Black Rock, exposed at low water but covered at high tide. An eccentric, Mr Trefusis of Trefusis, one day invited his wife to go boating with him to the Black Rock and picnic there. When he had landed her, he made his bow and rowed away with: 'Madam, we are mutually tired of each other and you will agree with me that it were best to part'. Fortunately a fishing smack picked her off the rock just as the tide was flowing over and brought her back to Trefusis. 'Be hanged to you rogues', said the husband. 'I'd have given you a guinea each to let her drown. Now you shan't have a shilling from me.'

* * * * *

Two Dutch ships that had almost foundered in a storm once came limping into Falmouth Harbour, only to be boarded and seized by the wicked Lady Jane Killigrew of Arwennick House, at the head of a band of men. The ship was bound for Spain and two Spanish factors in charge of its valuable cargo were murdered and dumped overboard, but not before one of them

The Drustan Stone.

with his dying breath cursed Lady Jane, prophesying: 'My blood will linger with you until my death is avenged upon your own sons.'

When the news got out, the Sheriff of Cornwall seized Lady Jane and her band of ruffians and all were condemned to death. But though the men were executed on the walls of **Launceston** Castle, Lady Jane was pardoned by Queen Elizabeth I. The Spaniard's curse duly took effect, however. Her son was dissolute, and her grandson wasted all the Spanish treasure, so that he was forced to sell Arwennick House to his younger brother, Sir Peter. Sir Peter's son, George, another Killigrew of the same stamp, one evening in a tavern in Penryn drunkenly insulted one of his cronies. He in turn made some remark about Killigrew's great-grandmother being sentenced to be hanged. Swords were drawn and Killigrew was killed in the scuffle. With George, last of the Killigrews, the Spaniard's death was avenged.

OS 204: SW 8032. 8 miles (12 km) south of Truro. Black Rock, SW 834316.

Feock

The village takes its name from the saint to whom the church is dedicated, St Feoca. Of the old church, built in the thirteenth century, only the west tower remains, and perhaps the stumpy round-headed cross in the churchyard, which shows the crucified Christ with uncrossed feet. In the porch of the present, mainly nineteenth-century church are the old village stocks, with

holes in graduated sizes. It is a 'guide-book' joke that they were designed to hold three and a half people (there are seven holes).

OS 204: SW 8238. 4 miles (6 km) south of Truro, via A39, B3289 and minor road.

Fraddam

One of Fraddam's most famous inhabitants was the evil Witch of Fraddam, whose arch-enemy was the Enchanter of **Pengersick**. She set out to destroy him with a tub of poisoned water and a crock of hell-brew, but he turned the tables on her and she fell in her own tub. It immediately assumed the shape of a coffin and the Enchanter raised a whirlwind which whisked it into the air, the crock following after.

'Settled till the day of doom!' cried the Enchanter, and, sure enough, the Witch still floats up and down the coast in her coffin, with the crock bobbing along behind her. She is still making mischief, stirring up the sea with her ladle and broom till the waves are mountain high — and woe betide the fisherman who sees her!

OS 203: SW 5934. 2 miles (4 km) southeast of Hayle, on B3302 (Helston road).

Frenchman's Creek

There is no more evocative place on the Helford River than Frenchman's Creek, the setting of Daphne du Maurier's novel of the same name. *Frenchman's Creek*, published in 1941, gives an imaginary account of how this secluded and tree-lined tidal water got

The old village stocks at Feock.

22

Frenchman's Creek on the Helford River.

its name, which it bore by the time of the first edition Ordnance Survey 6 inch map of 1888. It is thought to derive from an incident involving a French ship (a 'Frenchman') in the eighteenth or early nineteenth century. These dry bones Daphne du Maurier clothed with infidelity, piracy, smuggling, jail-breaking, attempted murder, narrow escapes from death, and above all romantic love at the time of the Restoration.

OS 204: SW 7425. West of Helford, 6 miles (10 km) east of Helston, by minor road off B3293 to Mawgan, St Martin and Newtown-in-St Martin. From the Newtown-Manaccan road, a lane leads west through Kestle to Helston. Opposite Kestle Cottage, a footpath signposted to Frenchman's Pill leads along the creek and back to Kestle Cottage. Further up the lane, signposted 'Frenchman's Creek', is the start of the same route in reverse. National Trust.

Germoe

'S. Germoke's chair in the chirch yard' is first mentioned by that name in the sixteenth century. Now known both as St Germoe's Chair and King Germoe's Throne, it stands in the north-east corner of the churchyard, built against the wall. It is a little pillared sedilia, or seat, generally believed to be St Germoe's shrine, a crowned head above the central pillar possibly representing Germoe the 'king'.

Whether Germoe was either a king or a saint is doubtful. He seems rather to have been one of a band of Irish monks who settled for a time in Cornwall early in the Dark Ages. In the legend of St Breaca, patron saint of neighbouring **Breage**, however, Germoe is called a king. According to the legend, he and Breaca were brother and sister, and they are linked in a saying in Cornish:

Germoe a king,
Breage a midwife.

23

St Germoe's Chair.

OS 203: SW 5829. 5 miles (8 km) west of Helston on A394. Just beyond the church is St Germoe's Well, reconstructed in 1977. It is on the left-hand side of a bridle road, branching left off the road into Germoe village, 40 yards (34 metres) west of the bridge.

Giant's Frying Pan, Caerwynnen (Carwynnen)

In the middle of what is known locally as Frying Pan Field stands the Giant's Frying Pan, a megalithic burial chamber whose huge capstone was originally supported on three uprights. (This 10 ton 'roof' collapsed in 1834 and was restored, but it fell again in 1967.) Though no longer much like a frying pan, it still justifies its name by looking like something that only a giant could wield. The same suggestion of titanic strength lies behind its other name of **Giant's Quoit**.

OS 203: SW 650373. 2 miles (3 km) south

of Camborne, reached by lane off B3303 (Helston road), shortly before Praze-an-Beeble, to Caerwynnen and Troon. Frying Pan Field is just east of Caerwynnen, on the north side of the road. The burial chamber can be seen from the road over a field wall (though not from a car). AM.

Giant's Hedge

The Giant's Hedge near Lerryn (or Lerrin) is an earthen rampart about 7 miles (11 km) long. A folk-rhyme explains:

> Jack the Giant had nothing to do,
> So he made a hedge from Lerrin to Looe.

There is a tradition in Britain going back to the Dark Ages of giants or the god Woden as the builders of earthworks. Later, because the Christian church equated them with demons, their feats were attributed to the Devil, and this has happened here. In another version of the local rhyme, the Devil is the builder.

OS 201: SX 150569-189570, intermittent.

Near Lanreath, 5 miles (8 km) north of Looe on B3359. Most easily visible east of B3359 at Lanreath, and north of the minor road off B3359 from Lanreath to Trevollard farm. AM.

Giant's Quoits

The Giant's Quoit at Pawton is a prehistoric chamber tomb now consisting of seven wallstones and a huge capstone, originally 13 feet by 7 feet by 2½ inches thick (4 by 2 by 0.8 metres). At the time of construction it was supported by nine wallstones: it now balances on only three. Originally it was covered by a mound about 70 feet long by 50 feet wide (21 by 15 metres). Once this had weathered or been ploughed away, the megalithic tomb thus laid bare suggested to local people a gigantic 'coit' or quoit.

In Cornish tradition, this and other exposed structures of the type once called dolmens were explained as the playthings of giants. In the nineteenth century, however, the Pawton chamber was also known as the Devil's Coit, a reminder that, in northern medieval tradition, the Devil was a giant.

Of other burial chambers once known as the Giant's Quoit the best known is Lanyon Quoit, a huge granite capstone like a giant table, 19 feet (6 metres) long perched on three upright stones, each 8 feet (2.5 metres) high. Once you could have ridden a horse under the arch, but in 1815 it fell down and its height was reduced when it was set up again nine years later. Archaeologists believe it to be the remains of a neolithic burial chamber, and the longer north-south mound, still visible although overgrown, reputedly produced large human bones suggestive of a giant's.

In the mid nineteenth century, country people gave the same name to Mulfra Quoit, 'the Quoit of the Round Bald Hill', south of Zennor. Here three upright stones form a rectangular cist, and a large capstone rests with one end on the ground. It appears to have fallen, but it is possible that this was its original position and that it was an 'earth-fast' chamber tomb.

A particularly dramatic example of a Giant's Quoit is Trethevy Quoit, a burial chamber perhaps four millennia old. Again, the earthen mound that once covered it has gone, leaving it looking indeed like a giant's toy. It stands 9 feet (3 metres) high, and con-

Lanyon Quoit.

Trethevy Quoit.

sists of five standing stones surmounted by a huge sloping capstone.
Local people in the nineteenth century
also knew it as the Giant's House, a
name suggested by its construction.
The chamber is divided into two parts
by a great doorstone at the east end.
The inner part is sealed off except for a
small rectangular hole in the corner of
the doorstone, just big enough for the
passage of a corpse.

At Zennor, the burial chamber once
known as the Giant's Quoit had rather
more of a legend attached to it than the
other examples. It was supposed to
have been built by a giant and to be
immovable. In 1861, it narrowly escaped being converted into a cowshed,
a design nipped in the bud by the Reverend William Borlase, the vicar of
Zennor, for the sum of five shillings.
This episode strengthened local belief
that the quoit could not — or should
not — be moved. It was thought that if
this were done the stones would return
to their places of their own accord.

OS 200: SW 966696, Pawton Quoit. 2
miles (3 km) south-east of Wadebridge on
St Beock Downs, reached via A39 to
Whitecross, then minor roads to Haycrook
Farm. It stands 360 yards (330 metres)
north-west of the farm, in the second field
below the farm buildings, on agricultural
land. It is hard to reach except in winter.
AM. OS 203: SW 430337, Lanyon Quoit.
Parish of Madron, 3 miles (5 km) north-
west of Penzance on the east side of B3312,
halfway to Morvah. National Trust. OS
203: SW 453354, Mulfra Quoit. 2 miles (3
km) south of Zennor via B3306 towards St
Just, then the minor road for New Mill and
Penzance. A public footpath leads west off
the road over Mulfra Hill to the Quoit. OS
201: SX 259688, Trethevy Quoit. A mile
(2 km) north-east of St Cleer off B3254.
After St Cleer's Well, the road comes to a
T-junction at the bottom of the hill.
Straight ahead is a public right of way to
the Quoit. It can also be reached by turning left for Darite, then right, and right
again within half a mile (1 km) at the sign
for Trethevy Quoit. English Heritage. OS
203: SW 469380, Zennor Quoit. South-
east of Zennor, by a track to the right off
B3306 to St Ives. The track loops west-
wards to pass the Logan Stone and Zennor
Quoit, then rejoins the main track on to
Lady Downs. See also the Giant's Quoits
near St Keverne.

Godolphin Cross

In the hamlet of Godolphin Cross, the name of Jew's Lane Hill is said to commemorate a Jew who hanged himself on a tree there. He was buried under the road and was supposed to haunt it in the shape of a bull and of a fiery chariot. This curious superstition had been known 'for generations' at the time it was recorded in the 1890s, at which time the tree could still be pointed out.

OS 203: SW 6031. 4 miles (6 km) northwest of Helston via B3302 and minor roads west. Jew's Lane is sharp left off the minor road to Nancegollan opening opposite the Godolphin Arms.

Godrevy Point

From the headland of Godrevy Point, looking inland, one can see St Agnes' Beacon, **Carn Brea** and **Trencrom Hill** against the skyline. Seaward lies Godrevy Island. A lighthouse (now unmanned) has stood on the island since 1859, built in response to public outcry at the number of lives lost on the Stones, a mile-long reef on the far side. Wrecks include the galleon containing the personal belongings of Charles I on its way to France in 1649 on the day of the King's execution. Of the sixty passengers and crew, only a boy and a dog survived, and they were marooned on Godrevy Island for two days, living on rainwater and seaweed, until they were rescued by a boat from St Ives.

*OS 203: SW 5743. 5 miles (8 km) northwest of Camborne via the southbound A30, then B3301 to Portreath, passing through Gwithian. About ½ mile (1 km) north of Gwithian, a left-turn off the road leads on to Godrevy Point. Also Godrevy Walk (South West Coast Path) from Portreath to Gwithian, passing **Ralph's Cupboard** and **Hell's Mouth**. National Trust (coast).*

Goss Moor

In medieval Welsh romance, King Arthur hunted a magical boar, Twrch Trwyth, from Ireland across Wales into the Severn estuary, and down into Cornwall. Here Twrch Trwyth was driven into the sea, never to return, and Arthur rested. This story may explain why local tradition has long regarded Goss Moor as Arthur's favourite hunting ground. To this day, when the wind howls there, the king's hunting horn can be heard as he chases phantom deer.

Others explain the howling as Jan Tregeagle at **Roche Rock**. As one nineteenth-century author put it: 'The howls of the great spirit Tregeagle begging shelter at Roche and surcease from his endless tasks are among the weirdest sounds of the Cornish hills and moors.'

OS 200: SW 9459-9559 area, west of Roche on B3274 and crossed by A30 between Roche Station and Indian Queens.

Gunwalloe Church Cove

Standing alone in the cove, under the lee of a cliff, is the 'Church of the Storms' founded in the sixth century by St Winwaloe or Gunwalloe. Of his original church nothing remains, for successive buildings on this site have been engulfed by sand or washed away by the sea. The present church was built in the fourteenth and fifteenth centuries, traditionally by the survivor of a shipwreck who vowed that in thanksgiving for his life he would build a church where the sound of prayer and the voice of the sea would mingle.

Inside the church, serving as inner doors, are painted panels from a sixteenth-century roodscreen made from the wreckage of the *St Anthony of Lisbon*. This, the most famous victim of the many shipwrecks in Church Cove, was the King of Portugal's carrack, wrecked in 1526. Its fabulous cargo, worth £18,880 in the money of the day, vanished without trace.

It became the subject of a Royal Commission and John Milliton of Pengersick, William Godolphin and Thomas St Aubyn were all accused of being involved. Some say there is evidence to suggest that the treasure was at one time bricked up within the walls of **Pengersick Castle**. However, no single item from the ship's inventory (which survives) was ever seen again, though gold coins found in the sand of Church Cove from time to time are said to have come from the wreck.

OS 203: SW 6620. 4 miles (6 km) south of Helston on the west side of the Lizard Peninsula, via A3083, then minor road to Berepper and Gunwalloe. From Gunwalloe, the road continues to Chyanvounder and past the Halzephron Inn to Winnianton Farm. Footpath thence to Church Cove. National Trust.

Halliggye Fogou

The most impressive of Cornwall's fogous or souterrains is Halliggye Fogou, an underground stone-lined gallery 54 feet (16.5 metres) long. The passage-like fogous, found both in Britain and Ireland, remain enigmatic. They have been variously explained as 'earth houses', refuges or cold storage places serving iron age villages. To country people in Cornwall in the nineteenth century, they were known only as 'old men's workings'. As in Scotland, they were linked with the supernatural. They were often believed to run immeasurably far underground, as at **Boleigh Fogou** and at Pendeen Vau, where on Christmas morning a White Lady with a red rose in her mouth would give news of her native land brought through submarine passages connecting the fogou with Ireland. At Halliggye there is no Irish lady — but the fogou does run far underground, and it *is* dark and spooky.

OS 203: SW 714239. 5 miles (8 km) southeast of Helston off B3293, near Garras.

Easiest access through the lodges of Trelowarren off B3293, opposite the road to Trevassack. By tarmac road through Trelowarren Plantations to Chybilly farm, then by track left to Halliggye hamlet. A narrower track right of the old thatched house of Halliggye leads to the site. Over the stile, turn left. The fogou is in the small fenced area. Torch needed. English Heritage. Pendeen Vau, SW 384355, in the grounds of Pendeen House and permission to visit needed (AM).

Helford River

Helford River is reputed to be the home of Morgawr, the Helford monster, a smaller version of Nessie. Described as a hideous hump-backed creature with stumpy horns, Morgawr has been sighted many times since 1926 and in February 1976 was photographed from Rosemullion Head near Falmouth.

* * * * *

Early in September 1840 a smuggling vessel named the *Teignmouth*, on ap-

Halliggye Fogou.

proaching land, saw two men on the beach. The crew asked them to help land their cargo — 133 kegs of brandy which were attached to the outside of the ship. The men agreed but, once the goods were landed, drew their pistols and declared themselves to be coast-guards from the Coverack station. The smugglers were too few to resist, and the coastguards seized both brandy and ship. The brandy was sub-sequently taken to the Customs House at Helford. The smugglers, however, were not about to give up their prize. At about one o'clock on the morning of 18th September, about thirty or forty men assembled at Helford, forced their way into the Customs House and car-ried off all the kegs save three from the cellar. The man and wife who lived there heard the smugglers at work but were afraid to raise the alarm, espe-cially as the Customs House was half a mile (1 km) from the nearest help.

OS 204: SW 7526 area. 6 miles (10 km) east of Helston by minor road off B3293 to St Keverne. Rosemullion Head: SW 7927.

Hell's Mouth

Beyond **Ralph's Cupboard**, the coastal path from Portreath runs past a spectacular cliff with a sheer drop of 200 feet (60 metres) to the sea. It is aptly named Hell's Mouth: this in-hospitable coast has proved literally the gateway to the Otherworld for many a fisherman. More than this, it belongs to a long Atlantic seaboard tra-dition of connecting coastal features with Hell: collapsed sea caves are known as 'the Mouth of Hell' (*Bocca del Inferno*) as far apart as Portugal and Shetland.

*OS 203: SW 606431. 4½ miles (7 km) from Portreath, on the north side of B3301 (Portreath-Hayle road), on Hudder Down. On the South West Coast Path from Portreath to **Godrevy Point**. National Trust (coast).*

Helston

This old market town is supposed to have got its name from a block of stone that lay for many years in the yard at the Angel Inn. Some say it once blocked the mouth of Hell and was carried here by the Devil when he came to Cornwall. On his way he was chal-lenged by the town's patron saint, his age-old enemy St Michael. In the com-bat that ensued the Devil dropped the stone, which gave its name — Hell Stone — to Helston. The name of the inn allegedly commemorates this visi-tation by the archangel.

Today the famous Hell Stone is no longer in one piece: it was broken up in 1783 for building purposes, probably by the publican, R. Thomas. Its rem-nants are built into the west wall of the Angel (now the Angel Hotel). They consist of two lumps of black rock, which analysis has shown to be meta-gabbro and not meteoric in origin as has been claimed. Both pieces are marked by grooves, evidently from the wheels of coaches passing over it in the days when it lay on the ground in the inn courtyard.

It is a family tradition among descend-ants of Mary Ann Bennetts, licensee of the Angel to 1875, that the Hell Stone would bring tragedy on any woman living at the inn. This curse was held to explain the death of her two sons in 1873 during a smallpox epidemic, the death of her granddaughter's husband, and thirty years later the drowning of her great-grandson.

More cheerfully, it was to celebrate their saint's victory over the Devil that the people of Helston are supposed to have first danced the Furry Dance, originally on 8th May, the feast of St Michael (now the nearest Saturday).

OS 203: SW 6527. 15 miles (24 km) south-west of Truro, on A394. The Angel Hotel is in the town centre. The remains of the Hell Stone are in the alley to the right of the Angel, set under a window in the wall of the inn.

The Hurlers stone circle.

The Hurlers

This is the name long given to three fine bronze age stone circles in a line, almost touching one another, on Craddock Moor. The circles consist of thirteen, seventeen and nine surviving stones. Standing somewhat aloof west-south-west of the midmost circle are two stones known as the Pipers.

A tradition at least as old as the sixteenth century accounted for the stones as men turned to stone for profaning the Lord's Day by hurling. Hurling matches, peculiar to Cornwall, were played between two teams of forty to sixty men a side. The object was to carry off a wooden ball to one's home goal, sometimes several miles away. Cornishmen seem to have taken no notice of the dire warning the Hurlers presented: well into the nineteenth century, hurling matches were usually played on Sunday afternoons.

If the Pipers seem a little out of place in this sporting context, it is because they belong to a different tradition. In Cornwall, as elsewhere, stone circles are usually identified as dancers — for example the **Merry Maidens**.

An old belief is that the Hurlers could not be counted. This 'countless stones' superstition is very ancient and is attached to several stone circles in Britain, notably Stonehenge.

*OS 201: SX 258714. ¹/₂ mile (1 km) north-west of Minions off B3254. Approaching via St Cleer's Well (St Cleer) or Trethevy Quoit (Darite), the minor road into Minions passes the Longstone (stone cross, SX 255705) on the right. Shortly after this, a track to the left before the village is signposted to the Hurlers. (This very rough track continues past the **Cheesewring**.) English Heritage.*

Jamaica Inn

On Bodmin Moor is the isolated Jamaica Inn, made famous by Daphne du Maurier's novel of the same name. Once a notorious haunt of smugglers, in the pages of *Jamaica Inn* it becomes the headquarters of a ruthless gang of wreckers.

One of the charges against the notorious Cornish wreckers was that they showed false lights to lure ships on to the rocks. They are said to have done this by hobbling a horse and tying a lantern round its neck. As it moved

The Pipers.

slowly along the clifftop, the lantern bobbed like a ship's light at sea, giving other ships the illusion that they were far from the shore. This practice was known as 'to jibber the kibber'.

Whether the allegation that they lured ships to their doom is true or false, wreckers figured in the English national press of the eighteenth and early nineteenth centuries as depraved

Jamaica Inn.

men — and also women — who, if they did not cause the tragedies of others, exploited them. In March 1751, when a ship carrying the figurehead of the Duke of Cumberland was wrecked near Porthleven and all her crew were drowned, the *General Evening Post* reported that 'the cliffs as usual were covered with hundreds of greedy Cormorants, waiting for their prey, which no sooner came within their reach, but was swallowed up by them, more Barbarous in their nature than Cannibals'.

Such are the traditions Daphne du Maurier wove into her portraits of Joss Merlyn, landlord of Jamaica Inn, and his evil gang. Her vivid account of a wrecking is true to the spirit of reports in the more sensationalist newspapers: 'They chattered and squabbled like monkeys, tearing things from one another … When the first body was washed ashore … they clustered around it, diving amongst the remains with questing, groping hands, picking it clean as a bone; and, when they had stripped it bare, tearing even at the smashed fingers in search of rings, they abandoned it again, leaving it to loll upon its back in the scum where the tide had been.'

Tame by comparison are the two ghosts the inn now reputedly harbours, a man in a tricorne hat, and a murdered sailor who sits on an outside wall.

OS 201: SX 183768. Near Bolventor, on A30 from Launceston to Bodmin.

Kilkhampton

Kilkhampton church is the setting of the once famous *Meditation among the Tombs* by the religious writer James Hervey (1714-58). 'It was an *antient Pile*; reared by Hands, that, Ages ago, were mouldered into Dust. … The deep *Silence*, added to the gloomy Aspect, and both heightened by the Loneliness of the Place, greatly increased the *Solemnity* of the *Scene*.'

After this beginning, worthy of a Gothick novelist, he reflects sombrely on the monuments of the dead, finally coming to that of a warrior whose excellence 'is written on the Minds of his Countrymen'. The monument belongs to Cornwall's great Civil War hero Sir Bevil Grenville (or Beville Granville), killed at the battle of Lansdowne (1643). Sir Bevil's fame was spread far beyond Cornwall by the Reverend Stephen Hawker of **Morwenstow** in the rousing 'Gate-Song of Stowe' in his *Cornish Ballads* (1869):

> Call the hind from the plough, and the
> herd from the fold,
> Bid the wassailer cease from his revel:
> And ride for old Stowe, where the banner's
> unrolled,
> For the cause of King Charles and Sir
> Beville. …
> Ay! by Tre, Pol, and Pen, ye may know
> Cornish men,
> 'Mid the names and nobles of Devon; —
> But if truth to the King be a signal, why
> then
> Ye can find out the Granville in heaven. …

OS 190: SS 2511. 4 miles (7 km) northeast of Bude on A39.

King Arthur's Hall

King Arthur's Hall is a mysterious prehistoric monument on Bodmin Moor consisting of a rectangular enclosure, about 60 feet by 35 feet (18 by 11 metres), lined with slabs of moorstone. It was linked with Arthur by the time of cartographer John Norden (1548-1626), who made an engraving of it. Like many places long associated with Arthur, it fits less with the medieval king of romance than with folk traditions of Arthur as more than human.

OS 200: SX 129777. Near St Breward, 4 miles (6 km) south of Camelford, via A39, then B3266 for St Tudy. A minor road east off B3266 leads to St Breward Churchtown. From the church, the road continues to St Breward proper, forking before it joins the main road through the village. The north fork continues across the road to become an intermittently fenced road across Church Hay Down, to Hallagenna farm, and then

across Lady Down. At the crossing of two unfenced roads, the north fork is presently met by a farm track also breaking north, to Irish. A public footpath leads from this track east past a cairn and continues north-east, then east, past King Arthur's Hall. Marked on OS Pathfinder map 1338 (Bodmin Moor west).

King Doniert's Stone

This ancient stone is part of a decorated cross-shaft bearing the words DONIERT ROGAVIT PRO ANIMA ('Doniert ordered [this] for the good of his soul'). The Doniert whose grave it marks was probably King Durngath of Cornwall, who was drowned in the river Fowey in about AD 875.

OS 201: SX 238688. A mile (2 km) north-west of St Cleer by public footpath off B3360 to Doublebois. English Heritage.

Lamorna

Mermaid's Rock near Lamorna took its name from a legendary mermaid

The sign of the Lamorna Wink inn.

who once haunted the spot and whose singing foretold shipwreck. Many fishermen were lured to the rock by the sweetness of her song but were never seen again. It is a 'half-tide rock' like the one on which another mermaid was stranded near **Cury**.

Locals say that the pub is called Lamorna Wink from the days when it was licensed only as an alehouse and this was how a client indicated that he required something stronger!

OS 203: SW 4424. 4 miles (6 km) south-west of Penzance by minor road south off B3315 from Penzance to Land's End. The pub is in the middle of the village. Mermaid's Rock is in Lamorna Cove, SW 455238.

Landewednack (Lewednack)

Landewednack parish church is dedicated to St Wynwallow, the same Winwaloe or Gunwalloe who founded the church at **Gunwalloe Church Cove**. To the right of St Wynwallow's very pretty porch, with its round-headed doorway and maidenhair ferns, is a low slate headstone bearing this inscription:

> Mourn not
> for me my Paren[ts]
> Dear, I am not dead
> but sleeping here, my
> debt is paid and I am free, therefore pre-
> [pare to follow me].

(Part of the inscription is buried, but a half-broken slab left of the path to the porch completes the message.)

Behind this memorial is another slate headstone with an even sterner reminder to grief-stricken parents of the promises of their religion:

> Let
> Parents learn to be
> content, when God
> requires that is but lent,
> in youth, nor Childhoo[d]
> put no trust, for all
> [m]ust Dye that come from dust.

Landewednack (Lewednack)

This was intended to reconcile the Williamses to the loss of their baby son, Benjamin, who was born and died in 1755. What different feelings must have attended the obsequies of Thomas Cole, Landewednack's rector, said to have been buried in 1683 'aged above 120'.

OS 203: SW 712127. 1 mile (2 km) north-east of Lizard Point, by minor road. Landewednack, sometimes written as well as pronounced 'Lewednack', is the name of a parish and appears on the map only as such. St Wynwallow's Church is at Church Cove and is signposted from Lizard.

Land's End

At this most westerly point of the English mainland there are spectacular views over the sea towards the Isles of Scilly. The flash of Seven Stones Light Vessel can be seen from here by night, marking the last visible remains of a lost country. These are the Seven Stones rocks, whence fishermen in the sixteenth century often dredged up in their nets what were apparently the remains of houses.

Cornish legend said that between Land's End and Scilly lay a tract of land containing 140 parishes. This was suddenly overwhelmed by a great flood and only one man escaped, an ancestor of the Trevilians (later Trevelyan). He was carried to the shore by his horse ahead of the advancing waves and reached safety in a cove at Perran. Old fishermen used to declare that on clear days and moonlit nights they had often seen the roofs of the churches and houses of the lost land under the water. Later this lost land was connected with Arthurian Lyonnesse, the home of Tristan.

OS 203: SW 3425. 8 miles (13 km) south-west of Penzance, on A30. The Seven Stones light-vessel can be recognised by its 'character': three white flashes every 30 seconds, each flash of 0.5 seconds duration,

with eclipses of 4.5, 4.5 and 19.5 seconds respectively.

Launceston

In the Roman Catholic Church of the English Martyrs can be seen the shrine of St Cuthbert Mayne, an English priest during the reign of Elizabeth I who joined the household of Francis Tregian at Golden Manor. There, disguised as a steward, he secretly ministered to Catholics of the neighbourhood until 8th June 1577, when Richard Grenville with a hundred armed men arrested him and most of Tregian's household. Mayne was later tried and executed in Launceston, though one of the justices had complained to the Privy Council that Grenville had intimidated the jury. Mayne's skull is still preserved as a relic in the Carmelite convent at Lanherne. Formerly known as the Blessed Cuthbert Mayne, he was canonised as one of the Forty Martyrs of England and Wales by Pope Paul VI in 1970.

OS 201: SX 3384. 20 miles (32 km) north-west of Plymouth on A388. The church is half a mile north of the town at St Stephen's Hill on the Bude Road.

The Loe

The Loe, a long, brackish freshwater lake, was created when the sandspit of Loe Bar formed across Helston's harbour mouth in the thirteenth century. Tradition says this was the work of Jan Tregeagle of **Dozmary Pool**. Like Dozmary, the Loe claims to be the lake to which Sir Bedivere bore King Arthur after his last battle, and where, at Arthur's command, he cast away the marvellous sword Excalibur. However, if Arthur was a real man, he probably lived in the sixth century, so the Loe is of too recent formation for this story to be true.

OS 203: SW 6424. 1 mile (2 km) east of Porthleven on the west coast of the Lizard

The Roman Catholic Church of the Martyrs, Launceston.

Loe Bar and the Loe.

The Longstone.

peninsula. *Access by footpath from Porthleven or by minor road off A3083 south of Helston to Tangies, then footpath along Carminowe Creek. National Trust.*

The Longstone

A saint (some say St Austell) was returning to his cell across St Austell Downs one night when a wind conjured up by the Devil blew his hat away. Thrusting his staff in the ground, he went racing after the hat but could not catch it. Unable to find his staff in the dark, he went home to his cell. Next morning, when he went to look for his hat and staff, he found that the Devil had turned them both to stone.

The Saint's, or as it was often known, the Giant's Hat, a round boulder, was removed in 1798 by soldiers who believed it was causing the rain that was making their camp wet. His staff, a tall pillar known as the Longstone, used to stand on Longstone Downs, north-west of St Austell, but was moved in 1970 in the course of work by China Clays and re-erected in Roche.

OS 204: SW 988603. In Roche, 5 miles (8 km) north of St Austell via A391 and B3274, in front of the Old People's Bungalows, Harmony Close, off Harmony Road (signposted to St Dennis and Nanpean). For an idea of the original site and to see a lunar landscape, take A391 out of St Austell in the direction of Bodmin. Shortly before the road passes under the railway line, a narrow street leads off left, skirting the railway line, then passing under the railway through a double tunnel. The road climbs steeply to Trenance Downs, and continues over Longstone and Hensbarrow Downs to join B3274 to Roche. The site of the Longstone was west of the road at SW 984562.

Ludgvan

The church is said to have been founded by St Ludgvan, an Irish missionary, who also made a well by diverting a stream into the sacred precinct. He granted its waters the power of protecting any child baptised with it from being hanged by a hempen rope. So firm was belief in this virtue that people came for miles to have their children baptised here. When a Ludgvan woman convicted of murder *was* hanged with such a rope, it came as a great shock to Ludgvan people. However, on searching the parish register, they found the explanation: she had been christened elsewhere. There *was* a catch — experience is said to have shown that St Ludgvan's blessing did not extend to a noose of silk.

OS 203: SW 5033. 2 miles (3 km) northeast of Penzance, via A30 and then B3309 from Crowlas. This route passes the Giant's Grave, SW 505322-508324, west of A30 shortly after its roundabout junction with A394, straddling the minor road through Varfell to Ludgvan.

Madgy Figgy's Chair

Madgy Figgy's Chair is a chair-shaped rock near Tol-Pedn-Penwith perched on a columnar pile of rocks known as Chair Ladder. It was here that Madgy Figgy, one of the notorious **St Levan** witches, would be seen sitting when storms were raging and ships about to be wrecked.

People said that she herself would raise the storms. Many great tempests were attributed to the black arts, and conversely, into the nineteenth century, around the British coast there were men and women who made a living peddling *fair* winds to sailors and fisherman. In the 1860s the Cornishman John Suttern still sold winds but lamented that 'trade had grown unprofitable', as steamships did not need them.

The original Madgy Figgy may have sold winds in this way, but later imagination took over: from her chair she was supposed to fly to Spain, mounted on a stem of ragwort, a favourite steed of witches.

OS 203: SW 365216 (Tol-Pedn-Penwith). South-west of St Levan, beyond Porthgwarra, along the South West Coast Path.

Marazion

A few years before the end of the eighteenth century a young sportsman on Marazion Green with his fowling-piece on his shoulder saw a raven and took a shot. An old man who was nearby rebuked him, saying he ought on no account to have shot a raven, because King Arthur was still alive in that form. Cervantes' Don Quixote mentions this tradition nearly two centuries earlier: he had heard that the king was turned into a raven by magic and that in the fulness of time he would recover his kingdom and reign again — 'for which reason it cannot be proved, that, from that time to this, any Englishman has killed a raven.'

OS 203: SW 5130. 3 miles (4 km) east of Penzance by minor road off A394 to Helston.

Mawgan (St Mawgan-in-Meneage)

According to tradition, St Mawgan's Church was formerly at Carminowe at the end of the parish. But giants used to come at night to the graveyard and dig up the corpses. The villagers tried to trap the giants by digging pits and covering them with 'sprouse' (light hay or grass). The ruse failed, however, so they adopted the expedient of moving the church out of the giants' reach.

Perhaps the story reflects resistance by local pagans to the activities of St Mawgan. Mawgan Cross, on the village green, dates from AD *c*.600 and may have been used by this Welsh bishop from Pembrokeshire as a preaching cross before he founded the first church.

The present church was begun in the twelfth or thirteenth century and inside are the lifesize effigies of Sir Roger Carminowe and of his lady, Johanna. Sir Roger, who as a young man went on the last crusade in 1270, claimed descent from King Arthur. He died

Mawgan (St Mawgan-in-Meneage)

and was buried at Carminowe in 1308: the effigies were brought here three centuries later.

What rancour and indignation are perpetuated in stone on a sarcophagus, left of the path to the church porch, which bears this inscription:

THIS MONUMENT WAS ERECTED
AT THE EXPENSE OF M^{RS} ANN INGERSOLL
the widow of Lieut Joseph Lander
as a Memorial of Esteem and Respect for her Relative
JAMES LANDER GENT.
whose Property
she and her Family succeeded in retaining
after an Expensive Law-suit
promoted by his distant relatives
but which by a sentence of the Judge of the Court
was proved to be groundless
and fallacious.

OS 203: SW 7025. 1 mile (2 km) south of Gweek via B3293 towards St Keverne and minor road. Mawgan Cross, SW 707248 (AM). Note also the memorial to John Trounson left of the path to the porch.

Mên-an-Tol.

Mên-an-Tol

The name of the Mên-an-Tol, near Morvah, means 'the stone of the hole', but once it was more ominously known as the Devil's Eye. It is the middle stone in a line of three and was possibly the 'porthole' entrance through which remains were placed in a neolithic burial chamber.

A farmer told the antiquary William Borlase, when he visited it in 1749, that people crept through the hole to cure pains in the back and limbs. Children were also passed through the hole to cure rickets, three or nine times (magical numbers) and widdershins (magical direction).

Many people believed that the stone was an oracle and that any question put to it by laying two brass pins across each other on the top edge of the stone would be answered by their acquiring a mysterious motion.

The Merry Maidens.

OS 203: SW 427349. In the parish of Madron, 4 miles (6 km) north-west of Penzance, by minor road from Madron towards Morvah. Shortly after Lanyon Farm, a farm track used as a public footpath leads off right for just over ¹/₂ mile (1 km) to Mên-an-Tol.

Merry Maidens

The Merry Maidens is Cornwall's most perfect stone circle. The Cornish name for it is *Dawns Mên* ('the dancing stones') and a local belief that the stones are dancers turned to stone goes back to at least *c*.1730.

The usual tale is that the nineteen standing stones, each about 4 feet (1.2 metres) high, are girls turned to stone for dancing on a Sunday. The musicians who played for them — the Pipers of Boleigh, two tall stones 15 feet (4.5 metres) and 13¹/₂ feet (4 metres) high, standing in a field not far off — were likewise turned into stone after trying to escape.

Several sets of Nine Maidens and also the Trippet Stones likewise stand for all to see as victims of divine retribution for dancing on Sunday. Stone circles throughout Britain and in parts of Europe were traditionally explained as people — mostly women — turned to stone for profaning the sabbath by dancing. An exception is the **Hurlers**.

Though the sabbath-breaking story is connected with a popular medieval sermon against dancing on holy days in churchyards, the idea of the stones as dancers itself is probably older: Stonehenge was called 'the Giant's Dance' already by the twelfth century, the image being suggested by the carol or ring dance.

*OS 203: SW 433245, 435247 and 425282. Near **Lamorna**, 4 miles (6 km) south of Penzance. Pipers of Boleigh on the right of B3315 from Penzance to Land's End, shortly after Trewoofe (see **Boleigh Fogou**). On farmland, but visible from road. The Merry Maidens are a little further on, on the right, and accessible. AM. Nine Maidens, near St Stithians (OS 203: SW 683365); near St Columb Major (stone row, OS 200: SX 937676); and near Boskednan (Pathfinder 11364, St Ives & Penzance North: SW 435351). Trippet Stones, on Manor Common between Temple and Bradford (OS 200: SX 131750). All AM.*

Mevagissey

The churchyard has an extraordinary number of fine gravestones, often of slate and with well executed lettering (though not always the best spelling and grammar). As one might expect, seafaring tragedies are frequently re-

Richard Dyer's gravestone at Mevagissey.

corded. Beside the back path to the church, running past the tower, are the memorials of the Over family. The stone dedicated to John Over and his wife Eliza also commemorates 'JOHN their eldest Son who was Lost by the foundering of the Ship Wennington in the Java Seas. Jan[y] 1878. Aged 45 years.' Another stone recalls another John 'supposed to be drowned on his Voyage from Mevagissey to Portsmouth Oct.[r] 29.th 1812'.

At the east end of the church is the gravestone of Richard Dyer, also recording the loss of his son, William, 'unfortunately drowned off Holyhead; Nov.[r] 28th 1849; Aged 18 Years':

Low in the caverns of the deep,
Beside some coral bed he lies;
Wrapt in the sea weeds there to sleep,
Till from the grave of death he rise;
Yes, he who came to bless and save,
Shall rise [sic] him from this watery grave.

On the south side of the church, family heartbreak lies all round in poetic epitaphs commemorating a young father (Walter Giles, died 25th August 1775), a mother with two of her children (Elizabeth Over, died 22nd November 1772) and two grandparents with their little grandson (Joseph and Mary Elvins, with Joseph, died 31st January 1870, aged three years and nine months):

During the few short years of life,
He was a happy child;
Because he was so kind and good.
So gentle and so mild.

OS 204: SX 0144. 5 miles (8 km) south of St Austell on B3273. Mevagissey church is signposted left, up Church Lane.

Morwenstow

The Reverend Robert Stephen Hawker, vicar of Morwenstow, was a poet and eccentric, who used to take his pig with him on his parish rounds. When in 1837 he built Morwenstow vicarage, he had the kitchen chimney shaped like his mother's tomb. The other chimneys were models of church towers that had taken his fancy, complete with castellations, turrets and fake windows.

Hawker was the originator of the Harvest Festival — an idea which his fellow clergy at the time roundly condemned as pagan — and his poems include the rousing 'Song of the Western Men':

A good sword and a trusty hand!
A merry heart and true!
King James's men shall understand
What Cornish lads can do.

It was Hawker's idea, when a mass grave had to be dug for forty of the crew of the *Caledonia*, wrecked in 1843, to place the ship's figurehead on it. This represents a Scotsman in a kilt, wielding a claymore, though in a poem on the disaster Hawker calls it 'fair Scotland's figured form', the personification of Scotland as Caledonia:

> She watches by her bold, her brave,
> Her shield towards the fatal sea:
> Their cherished lady of the wave
> Is guardian of their memory.

Male or female, the figurehead gave rise to a local belief that if anyone walked too near it at midnight the claymore would descend and cut off their heads.

When Hawker came to Morwenstow in 1836, he brought with him a bedstead of Spanish chestnut which was set up in a room overlooking the churchyard. In that churchyard, halfway down the main path, was the tomb of 'John Manning and Christiana his wife, who died AD 1546, without issue'. John Manning was a local landowner and Christiana Kempthorne the vicar's daughter. Only five months after their marriage, John was gored to death by a bull not far from their house. At the shock of seeing his corpse,

This kilted Scotsman, once the figurehead of the 'Caledonia', surmounts the grave at Morwenstow of those who died when the ship was wrecked in 1843.

Christiana gave premature birth to their child, and both she and the baby died. Only after coming to Morwenstow did Hawker discover that the Spanish chestnut bed was the very marriage bed of John and Christiana, with their names carved on it. The two surviving memorials of this unhappy pair had accidentally been brought together.

A far cry from Hawker is 'Cruel Coppinger'. David Coppinger was a Dane, the captain of a ship driven into Harty Race during a terrible storm. Unable to reach the haven of Harty Pool, Coppinger dived overboard and battled his way to shore. A young woman called Dinah Hamlyn had ridden down to the beach to watch the wreck, and silently Coppinger leapt up with her on her horse and made her take him home. He remained in Dinah's house and, when her father died a year later, married her.

Coppinger became the leader of a ruthless gang of smugglers. He established a reign of terror in the Morwenstow neighbourhood, seizing control of local roads and ordering others off them at night time. Still known as 'Coppinger's Tracks', they lead to the headland of Steep Brink, below which, in an almost inaccessible cove, the gang's contraband was stored. So feared was Coppinger that, when Dinah gave birth to an idiot son, some believed that, because of his father's sins, the child had been born without a soul. Eventually, however, the 'Revenuers' descended on Morwenstow in force and in the ensuing fracas many of the smugglers were killed.

Coppinger himself departed, as he had come, in a violent tempest. But whereas his arrival in Morwenstow by shipwreck sounds like history, his departure has overtones of the *Flying Dutchman*. During the storm a strange vessel appeared off Harty Race and lowered a boat that battled through high seas to where Coppinger stood waving his cutlass and cursing on the beach. He boarded the boat, which fought its way back to the ship, and the ship vanished into the spray, Coppinger with it. 'Cruel Coppinger' was never seen again.

OS 190: SS 2015. 6 miles (10 km) north of Bude, via A39 and minor road from Crimp.

Mousehole

The Mousehole is easily accessible only by boat. 'The proper name of it is the Giant's Cave, only we do call it the Mouse's Hole', observed a nineteenth-century Penzance boatman.

Before reaching the Mousehole, there is a rock a little way out at sea called *Merlin Carreg*, now Merlyn Rock, respecting which there was an old prophecy given in 1602 in Cornish as:

> Ewra teyre a war meane Merlyn,
> Ara lesky Pawle, Pensanz ha Newlyn.

A local rhyme translates:

> There shall land on the rock of Merlin
> Those who shall burn Paul, Penzance
> and Newlyn.

This contingency seemed unlikely, as the rock is only partially uncovered even at low tide, but when in 1595 a Spanish fleet burned Mousehole to the ground the attack was regarded as the fulfilment of the prophecy.

The church register of Paul recorded: 'Jenken Keigwin of Mowsholl being kild by the Spaniards, was buried the 24th of Julij.' The cannonball said to have killed him was long preserved in the village. Also handed down were traditions concerning the attack, among them that a farmer's wife, finding a Spaniard drunk and asleep in a cornfield, cut his throat with a sickle. The name of Point Spaniard, down the coast from the Mousehole, commemorates the attack.

OS 203: SW 4626. 2 miles (3 km) south of Penzance via A30, B3315 to Newlyn and minor road through Paul. The Mousehole, SW 467258. Merlyn Rock, SW 469259. Point Spaniard, SW 467256.

Mullion

Mullion was once a great place for smuggling. One story tells how a Mount's Bay boat under the command of 'Billy of Praow' [Praa] brought a cargo of brandy ashore at Mullion Cove. The gun-brig *Hecate*, stationed in Mount's Bay, sent a boat to the scene and, taken by surprise, the smugglers abandoned their kegs. Later, however, large numbers of locals gathered and, breaking into an armoury at Trenance, equipped themselves with firearms and ammunition. Proceeding to the cliffs, they fired on the *Hecate*'s crew, forcing them to abandon the brandy and return to their ship. It is said that many respected citizens took part in this affair, but their disgraceful behaviour was subsequently hushed up.

OS 203: SW 6719. 5 miles (8 km) south of Helston, via A3083, then B3296 from Penhale.

Padstow

Doom Bar, the sandbank which choked Padstow Harbour and caused many shipwrecks, was reputedly the result of a curse laid by a mermaid after a local resident fired a shot at her while she was bathing.

OS 200: SW 9175. 5 miles (8 km) north-west of Wadebridge on A389. Doom Bar, SW 9277.

Pengersick Castle

Pengersick or Pengerswick Castle was in the eighteenth and nineteenth centuries a ruin consisting of a single tower, standing in a lonely hollow running down to Pengersick Cove. Many strange traditions concerning it existed among locals, mostly about 'Pengersick the Enchanter'.

One was that the heir of Pengersick returned from travels in eastern lands bringing with him a lady of great beauty thought to be a 'Saracen'. No

Padstow Harbour.

one apart from a few servants was allowed within the castle, and Pengersick himself would be closeted in his chamber for days on end and at night and during storms could be heard calling up spirits in some unknown tongue. The Saracen lady sat alone in her tower all day gazing out of a high window overlooking the sea. Her voice was seldom heard except when she sang to her harp, and then at dawn mermaids and strange spirits of the deep would be drawn to Pengersick Cove.

This mysterious pair long inhabited the castle. Years passed until one day a sunburnt stranger arrived in **Marazion**. Not long afterwards, on a violently stormy night, a burst of flames above the hill showed the people of Marazion that Pengersick Castle was ablaze. The castle's interior was utterly destroyed, and neither the Enchanter and his lady nor the dark stranger were ever seen again.

The legends of Pengersick the Enchanter probably began in the personality of Henry de Pengersick in the

fourteenth century, an excommunicant with a stormy relationship with the Church. The present castle came after his time, however, being built *c*.1500 as a fortified manor house. Later abandoned, it was a ruin, but for the tower, by 1738. Not surprisingly, there are rumours of secret passages connecting

Pengersick Castle.

the castle to the beach, and of the lost treasure of **Gunwalloe Church Cove** being bricked up within its walls.

OS 203: SW 578285. 5 miles (8 km) west of Helston, off A394 by minor road from Germoe to Praa Sands. Now a private residence, but visible from the road.

Penryn

A sensational murder is supposed to have taken place at a farm near Penryn called Bohelland, the fame of which was spread by a black-letter pamphlet, 'Newes From Perin in Cornwall: OF A most Bloody and vn-exampled Murther very lately committed by a Father on his owne Sonne (who was lately returned from the Indyes) at the Instigation of a mercilesse Step-mother. Together with their severall most wretched endes, being all performed in the Month of September last. Anno. 1618.'

The story it told was that, after years at sea, a young sailor returned to Penryn, having made his fortune. To surprise his parents, he at first pretended to all but his married sister to be a stranger. He took lodgings with his parents and was unrecognised, but they had fallen on hard times and murdered him for his money. Only the next day, when his sister came to share in the rejoicing at his return, did they realise what they had done and kill themselves out of remorse.

Stirring stuff, but did it happen? This same story has been reported as 'news' in several places, from Leipzig in 1618 (suspiciously the same year as at 'Perin') to Vienna as late as 1880. Whether the murder really took place or not, Penryn people later *thought* it had. Daniel and Samuel Lysons, who investigated the story for their *Magna Britannia*, reported in 1814: 'The site of the house is still pointed out; but the name of the family is not known.'

OS 204: SW 7834. 2 miles (3 km) north-west of Falmouth on A39. Bohelland farm is commemorated in street names in St Gluvias parish (SW 788347). A minor road leads from Penryn towards Mylor Bridge, becoming Church Hill, then Bohelland Road at the point where it makes a T with Bissom Road leading off right to Mylor. Off it run Bohelland Rise and Bohelland Way.

Pentillie Castle

A notable Cornish eccentric was Sir James Tillie of Pentillie Castle. He built himself a tower on the hill called Mount Ararat north of the castle and left instructions in his will that this was to be the place of his burial. He was to be dressed in his best clothes, with a wig and hat on his head, and seated in his chair, secured with iron bonds. Near him was to stand an oak chest with his books and papers, for within two years he would rise again and return to Pentillie. When he died in 1712, all was done as he directed, but within two years his flesh had been eaten by worms, his skeleton fallen from the chair, and his finery rotted. However, he is still in his tower, now decently enclosed from view inside a coffin.

The castle was demolished in 1968, but leaving a seventeenth-century wing from the Pentillie that Sir James Tillie knew.

OS 201: SX 407646. Just south of St Mellion, 3 miles (5 km) south-east of Callington on A338 (Launceston to Plymouth road), by minor road from Paynter's Cross. Mount Ararat, SW 406652.

Penzance

At the eastern end of the Esplanade, a small rocky peninsula jutting out into the sea is known as the Battery Rocks. Near the seaward end, in a recess in the rocks a little below high-water mark, a small natural basin of water about 3 feet (1 metre) deep was long known as the Barber's Pool. It was said to have got its name from a barber in the eighteenth century, who tied a stone round his neck and drowned himself in it.

Around the turn of the same century, a mansion in Chapel Street, near Penzance parish church, was badly haunted. The ghost was an old lady called Mrs Baines, shot by her gardener by mistake with a blunderbuss meant to deter boys from stealing her apples. Though more frightened than hurt, the old lady soon afterwards died, and from then on her ghost, a lace cap on her powdered hair and lace ruffles at her sleeves, was often seen in the garden, leaning on the gold-headed cane she had always carried. Inside the house, her high-heeled shoes were heard night after night tapping on the floors, or else her spinning-wheel whirring. For some time the mansion was unoccupied because of the haunting, but eventually it was divided into two, and Mrs Baines ceased to appear.

* * * * *

Real 'Pirates of Penzance' arrived in the town on the night of 29th September 1760. The townspeople were roused by the firing of guns, and soon after came the news that a strange ship was aground on the beach towards Newlyn. Crowding to the spot, they were alarmed by the sight of swarthy men armed with scimitars and rumours of Turkish atrocities put them in a panic. However, a group of volunteers got together and herded the 172 men (eight had been drowned) into a building known as the Folly.

By morning they had learned from the crew that the ship was 'an Algerine corsair', whose captain had run it aground accidentally whilst believing himself to be safely in the Atlantic at about the latitude of Cadiz (!). Once their fears of the 'Turks' had been allayed, the townsfolk became constant visitors, as the corsairs' exotic dress, their turbans, moustaches and long beards made them objects of wonder. They were on the whole treated kindly, until, after some delay, a ship of war returned them to Algiers.

OS 203: SW 4730. 24 miles (39 km) south-west of Truro on A30. Battery Rocks, SW 487296, shown by name on Pathfinder 1368 (Land's End & Newlyn).

Pistol Meadow

The approach down Pistol Lane to Pistol Cove, beneath the westward cliff of Lizard Point, gives no notice of the horrific secret about to be unfolded. It leads to a little grove of twisted tamarisks perched above the cove, with a wall on its landward side and stone steps leading up to the lighthouse.

In the mid eighteenth century, when it was just a rough meadow, a transport ship was wrecked off Lizard Point and a couple of hundred corpses were washed ashore. The Lizard people found them, jammed among the rocks at low tide, and near the reef on which the ship had foundered many pistols lay scattered.

Pistol Meadow.

The people dug pits in the meadow and, carrying the soldiers one at a time up the precipitous path from the cove, buried them in communal graves. It was slow work, taking days, and the cove began to be invaded by packs of hungry dogs. At last, however, every corpse lay safely in the graves in the meadow, thereafter known as Pistol Meadow. It is said that, for years afterwards, the people of Lizard could not bear to have a dog about. When the novelist Wilkie Collins visited the Point in the 1850s he saw no sign of one nor even heard one bark from any farmyard in the neighbourhood.

OS 203: SW 7012. South of Lizard, on A3083 from Helston. From Lizard car park, along Penmenner Road, to the left of the Top House. After about ¼ mile (400 metres), at a footpath sign, Penmenner Road turns into a track, which in turn leads to a bridleway called Pistol Lane. This meets the coast path at Pistol Meadow. National Trust (Pistil Meadow).

Polperro

On the western side of the harbour, in Chapel Cliff, is a cave known as Willy Willcocks' Hole. Willy Willcocks was a fisherman who, when exploring the cave, lost his way in the maze of tunnels. His ghost still roams the passages trying to escape.

On 19th April 1825 a Polperro fisherman hauling up his line found a keg of spirits attached to it. Casting about for more, he brought on board upwards of forty kegs, which he took to the Fowey custom house, where he received a reward. For several weeks the coast between Polperro and Fowey was the scene of similar 'catches'. The agents of the Wheal Howell mine, east of Fowey, had much trouble with miners in a permanent state of drunkenness. On 20th April all the men belonging to the mine succeeded in sneaking underground in pairs to where they had hidden a keg of brandy. They drank themselves into such a stupor that some of

them were brought to the surface again only with great difficulty.

OS 201: SX 2051. 3 miles (5 km) south-west of Looe via A387 and minor road through Crumplehorn. Chapel Cliff, SX 209507. Cornwall South Coast Path. National Trust.

Porthcadjack Cove

Near **Ralph's Cupboard** on the precipitous cliffs just west of Portreath is Porthcadjack Cove, once used for smuggling by William Burgess, a local farmer. Barrels of liquor were landed here at high tide and drawn up the cliff by pulleys. The contraband was stored at Trengrove Farm before being quietly moved to Burgess's buyers, for, like other smugglers, he had his regular customers. The liquor that came in of a dark night at Porthcadjack generally ended up being drunk at Tyacks Hotel in Camborne and the Plume of Feathers at Pool.

OS 203: SW 6445. Not far from Portreath, on the north side of B3301 (Portreath-Hayle road), along the South West Coast Path from Portreath to Godrevy Point. A lane running west from Portreath sea-front links with a footpath to West Point to join the Coast Path. National Trust (coast).

Porthcurno

Porthcurno was once haunted by a spectral ship. As the evening mists started to rise, a ghostly black square-rigger would come in from the sea and

glide up over the sands to continue on its way across dry land. Many people are reputed to have seen the ship, which was an omen of misfortune. Or was it? The unimaginative prefer to think that smugglers started this tale by coating their ships with luminous paint, to scare off intruders.

OS 203: SW 3822. 3 miles (5 km) south-east of Land's End off B3315 to Newlyn.

Porthgwarra

This tiny fishing hamlet was once known as Sweethearts' Cove. The story went that Nancy, a rich farmer's only daughter, and William, a poor sailor, were forbidden by her father to meet. Just before William's ship next sailed, however, he contrived to see Nancy and swore he would be forever true. As the months passed, she would watch for his ship from Hella Point, which people began to call Nancy's Garden.

No ship came; then one night Nancy heard William calling her and walked down to Porthgwarra Cove. An old

woman on the clifftop saw her sit on a rock at the water's edge and presently a young sailor appeared beside her. Though the tide rose and surrounded the rock, they did not move. The old woman shouted a warning, but they ignored her cry, all at once seeming to drift over the sea and vanish. News came next day that William's ship had been sunk; the beautiful Nancy's body was never found.

OS 203: SW 3721. 3 miles (5 km) southeast of Land's End, via B3315 then minor road from Polgigga.

Prussia Cove

This tiny haven for fishing boats gets its name from John Carter, a native of **Breage**, a celebrated smuggler. As a child in the mid eighteenth century he dubbed himself the 'King of Prussia' after Frederick the Great, then a popular hero. The nickname stuck to him all his life and his family home at Porthleah was called Prussia Cove because of it.

The Carter family — John's parents, seven brothers, two sisters and himself — were all involved in smuggling, and John was their leader. One of his most daring exploits was the robbery of Penzance Customs House, because some of the contraband seized and impounded there had already been promised to his customers.

OS 203: SW 5527. 6 miles (10 km) west of Helston, at end of lane leading south off A394 (Helston-Penzance road). South West Coast Path.

Ralph's Cupboard

A cleft in the rocks near Portreath is known as Ralph's Cupboard. It was formerly a cavern, the home of the giant Wrath. Wrath would lie in wait for fishing boats, and if they came within a mile of his hole he would wade out to sea, tie the boats to his belt and draw them into his den. There he would keep the well-fed among his victims to eat later — the skinny ones he tossed overboard. Ships in water too deep for

Ralph's Cupboard.

him to reach he would sink by slinging rocks on them from the cliff. These rocks can still be seen, showing above the water at ebb tide and forming a reef stretching away from Godrevy Head.

Long after the giant's death, the fishermen of St Ives continued to avoid the Cupboard. Eventually the roof fell in, leaving the present chasm. According to William Bottrell, writing in 1870, the place was formerly called the Giant's Zawn (meaning 'cave') and Ralph's Cupboard was a name 'of recent date', given after the Zawn had been used by Ralph, a famous smuggler. More likely 'Ralph' (once pronounced without the 'l') was mistakenly substituted for 'Wrath', which seems to be not a name but a Cornish term for 'giant'.

OS 203: SW 645452. ¹/₂ mile (1 km) from Portreath, on the north side of B3301 (Portreath-Hayle road), along the South West Coast Path between Portreath and Godrevy Point. A lane runs from Portreath sea-front (parking) west to chalets, whence a footpath leads towards West Point to join the coastal path. National Trust (coast).

Restronguet Creek

On the south side of Restronguet Creek stands the Pandora, Cornwall's oldest inn. Few inns enjoy such a picturesque site, overlooking the narrow tidal estuary opposite Restronguet Point, and few can boast such a history.

Parts of this low thatched house date from the thirteenth century, when there was a farm on the site. Later it became known as the Passage House, because a 'passing boat' or ferry was kept there, for the use of travellers on the Post Road, following the shortest route between Truro and Falmouth. At this stage in its history, it was the scene of a disaster, when the ferry boat sank and several people were drowned.

Subsequently the inn changed its name, first to the Ship, then to the Pandora, in memory of HMS *Pandora*, sent to Tahiti to bring back the mutineers of Captain Bligh's *Bounty*. The unlucky *Pandora* was wrecked on the Great Barrier Reef in 1791, with the loss of many of her crew and four of the prisoners. Her captain, Captain Edwards, was court-martialled on his return and dismissed the service. He retired to Cornwall, where he bought and renamed this inn. The figurehead of Pandora with her box, from which she let loose all the evils afflicting mankind, is mounted over the staircase.

OS 204: SW 814373. Pandora Inn, Restronguet Creek, Mylor Bridge, near Falmouth. 2 miles (4 km) north-east of Penryn, via Bissom Road to Mylor Bridge. From Mylor the road continues straight up the hill to the crossroads, across the Angarrick-Restronguet Barton road, then down Restronguet Hill (1:4) to Restronguet Passage. The Pandora Inn, signposted, is at the bottom, right on the creek.

The Rill

Northwards from Kynance Cove, a cliff path leads on to the Rill, the headland from which, at four o'clock in the afternoon of Friday 29th July 1588, the Cornish got their first sight of the Spanish Armada. On its summit is a heap of loose stones that may mark the base of the earliest lighthouse in Cornwall, built in the early seventeenth century.

Local people explained it differently: they called it the Apron String and said that the Devil once arrived with an apronful of stones to build a bridge across the Channel for smugglers. He was hurrying to the cliff edge when his apron string broke, scattering the stones on the ground, and he abandoned the whole project.

OS 203: SW 6813. 1 mile (2 km) north-west of Lizard Town, by public track and footpath off A3083. East side of Kynance Cove, National Trust. The Apron String (SW 674136) is marked 'Cairn' on Pathfinder sheet SW 61/71 (Lizard Point).

Roche Rock.

Roche Rock

Roche Rock, a strange outcrop of jagged schorl, rears fantastically above **Goss Moor**. Perched improbably on top are the ruins of St Michael's Chapel, licensed in 1409. It has a lower room for a chaplain or anchorite, and some said it was founded by St Roche. 'Roche', however, is simply French for 'rock': it was the rock that gave the village its name.

Legend says that the chapel and anchorite's cell were built as the refuge of the last of the Tregarricks, a leper. He lived there until his death, to avoid infecting others. He was brought food, drink and water to wash with every day by his daughter Gunett or Gundred. She fetched the water from a nearby well, still pointed out in the late seventeenth or early eighteenth century as St Gunett's Well.

The well disappeared, and Gunett was forgotten. Subsequently local lore claimed that the mysterious rock was the haunt of Jan Tregeagle after his escape from **Dozmary Pool**.

OS 200: SW 993595. 4 miles (7 km) north-west of St Austell, via A391 (Bodmin road), then B3274 to Roche. At the Rock Inn, a minor road leads east to Carbis. The Rock is south of the road, and there is a stone stile through the wall just beside the sign for Roche.

St Agnes

All around St Agnes are abandoned shafts from the great days of Cornish tin-mining. One of the mines was Polbreen Mine, haunted by the ghost of Dorcas, who committed suicide by throwing herself down the shaft. She made a nuisance of herself in the galleries, persistently calling the miners' names, so that they left off work to see who wanted them. Once, however, she saved a man's life, for he went to see who was calling him moments before a rock-fall crashed down on the spot where he had been standing.

OS 204: SW 7250. 6 miles (9 km) north of Redruth via A30, and then B3277 from Three Burrows.

50

St Anthony-in-Meneage

The granite in the tower of the little Norman church seems to have been imported from Normandy, so there may be some truth in the tale that it was built shortly after the Conquest by some Normans who were driven on to the Cornish coast by a storm. They vowed to St Anthony that, if he saved them, they would build a church on the spot where they landed. Their ship was blown into Durra Creek, where they fulfilled their vow.

OS 204: SW 7825. 8 miles (12 km) east of Helston via southbound A394, then A3083 to its junction with B3293. A minor road leads north-east off B3293 after Garras to Newton-in-St Martin, whence a lane leads to Manaccan and St Anthony.

St Columb Major

Though hurling has a long history in Cornwall (see the **Hurlers**) it survives in only two places, St Columb and St Ives. At St Columb it is played on two traditional days, Shrove Tuesday and the second Saturday in Lent. There are two teams, the Townsmen and the Countrymen. Which side players are on depends on where in the parish they live, and it is possible to change sides by moving. Though outsiders sometimes join in the early stages, later they fall out, leaving the match to the parishioners.

The game is played with a special ball the size of a cricket ball, made of applewood and covered with sterling silver. This is why it is sometimes referred to as 'Hurling the Silver Ball', though St Columb people call it simply Hurling. The ball is used until a new one is donated; the donor is then given the old ball as a souvenir.

The ball is thrown up at the beginning of the match, then tossed, hurled or carried over the ground, but never kicked. There are two ways of scoring, either to get the ball through one of the goals or to carry it right out of the parish. As the parish boundaries are further away than the goals, this is the more difficult method. The goals themselves are stone troughs: the Town Goal at Cross Putty, a mile (1.6 km) south-west of the Market Square; the Country Goal on the Wadebridge Road a mile to the north.

At the end of the game the winner is carried shoulder-high to the Market Square, where he 'calls-up' (i.e. calls in) the ball again at 8 pm, provided the game is over. The Hurling Song is sung and the ball is taken around the pubs, in each being dunked in a jug of beer, which becomes 'silver beer' to be drunk by the company.

OS 200: SW 9163. 6 miles (10 km) east of Newquay on A392.

Pictures in relief of a hand holding a silver ball, to be seen on bollards in St Columb Major, reflect the long history of hurling in this town.

St Dennis

In the story of King Arthur's birth, Duke Gorlois of Cornwall was away fighting at 'Dimilioc' when King Uther Pendragon lay with Gorlois's wife at **Tintagel** and Arthur was conceived. 'Dimilioc' is very likely St Dennis, where at the time of the Domesday Survey there was a manor called *Dimelihoc*. Another possible site is the iron age earthwork of Tregeare Rounds, marked on some old maps as 'Castle Demeliock'.

St Dennis may be a 'phantom' saint, rather than the St Denis who is patron of France, for the unusual circular churchyard wall possibly marks the line of an ancient hillfort, the *dinas* or 'stronghold', later confused with the saint's name.

OS 200: SW 9558. 5 miles (8 km) north-west of St Austell via A3058 and B3279 to Foxhole, St Dennis and Indian Queens. Tregeare Rounds (OS 200): SX 033800.

St Endellion

St Endellion, the daughter of a Welsh king, made her home in Cornwall, living as a hermit inland from Port Isaac. She was killed by a local landowner when her cow, on whose milk she lived, wandered on to his land. Dying, she asked to be put on a cart drawn by young cattle allowed to pull it wherever they liked. She wished to be buried where they stopped. On that spot St Endellion church was built, of granite shipped from Lundy Island. Her body is said to lie under the carved slate altar tomb placed there eight hundred years later.

OS 200: SW 997787. 6 miles (10 km) along B3314 from Wadebridge to Delabole. The church is on the left by the road.

St Germans

Strange noises heard on the air in the early hours of Sunday morning once made St Germans people draw the bedclothes over their heads, for they knew it was Dando and his Dogs passing. Dando was a priest of St Germans who was passionately fond of hunting. He and his companions were out hunting one Sunday and as they rode along they were joined by a strange huntsman. After a long hunt, seeing the stranger collect a large share of game, Dando disputed his right to it. When the stranger continued striking it to his saddle, Dando flung himself off his horse and grabbed at it. 'You shan't have it!' he cried. 'I'll go to hell for it

The shrine of St Endellion.

rather than you shall get it.' 'So you shall,' the stranger replied, and carried Dando off, the hounds following after in full cry.

When they reached the Lynher, he rode into the deepest pool with the hounds close behind and disappeared in a column of steam. This was the last anyone saw of Dando and his Dogs, but they can still be heard early on Sunday mornings, giving tongue as they race through the sky.

OS 201: SX 3657. 6 miles (10 km) south-east of Liskeard via A38, then B3249 from Tideford.

St Ives

On a hill south of the town is Knill's Steeple, a three-sided granite pyramid built by John Knill, a collector of customs at St Ives and in 1767 its mayor. He gave it out as his intention to be buried there, but in his latest will he requested that his body be given to surgeons for dissection. He was actually buried in Holborn, London.

Did Knill change his mind, or did he, as some suggest, use this pretext to build the spire as a landmark for shipping to help him in his secret career as a smuggler? Probably he simply recognised that St Ives needed a landmark — previously it had shared the church tower of St Hilary, in recognition of which it made St Hilary a yearly allowance of whitewash.

Whatever Knill's intentions, he left an estate to the corporation of St Ives to pay for the maintenance of the pyramid and for a ceremony to be per-

formed every fifth year on 25th July. Ten little girls dressed in white should dance through the streets to the spire, and there be joined by the mayor of St Ives and two widows. Everyone was to dance round the monument, then spectators sing the Hundredth Psalm. This eccentric bequest is still honoured, and for this service the girls receive £10 between them, the widows £2 each, and the fiddler who traditionally accompanies the dancing £1.

OS 203: SW 5140. 7 miles (12 km) north-east of Penzance, on B3311. Knill's Monument (SW 516386) is reached by turning off B3311 to Balnoon and Lower Vorvas, instead of continuing on to Halsetown. A public footpath runs part of the way round the hill on which it stands.

Knill's Steeple, St Ives.

St Keverne

Looking south-east from Manacle Point — and on a calm day watching for the tell-tale flash of surf — one can see the Manacle Rocks; looking landwards, the unusual octagonal spire of St Keverne's Church. Tower and spire were first built in about 1450, and when the latter was destroyed by lightning on 28th February 1770 it was immediately rebuilt because of its usefulness as a landmark. It gave ships notice of the Manacles, from Cornish *Maen Eglos*, 'the Church Rocks', so-called because of the value of St Keverne's spire as a warning.

Not all were given the chance to profit by it. The north-west area of the churchyard contains a number of mass graves of those who perished in shipwrecks on the coast of the parish. In October 1898 the SS *Mohegan* was wrecked on the Manacles with the loss of 106 passengers and crew, and their grave is marked by a large granite Celtic cross outside the north door of the church, near the tower.

On the other side of the path are three monuments, the middle one a small stone marking the site of the grave of 120 men, women and children who died when the emigrant ship *John*,

The gravestone of 120 people who were shipwrecked off the Manacles on 3rd May 1855.

on its way to Canada, struck the Manacles on 3rd May 1855. The captain was convicted of manslaughter and sent to prison, as were a number of St Keverne men for looting the victims.

To the right of this a cross marks the grave of officers and men of the VIIth Hussars, lost in the transport *Despatch*, wrecked on the Manacles on 22nd January 1800 as it was returning from the Peninsular War; to the left, another cross commemorates the officers and men who lost their lives when HM brig of war *Primrose* struck the Manacles on 22nd January 1809. (The *Primrose's* carronade, recovered by divers in 1978, stands in the south-west corner of the churchyard.) Perhaps 270 men, of whom 104 were buried in St Keverne churchyard, died in these two wrecks, having survived the war only to perish within sight of home.

OS 204: SW 7921. 9 miles (14 km) south-east of Helston on B3293. The Manacles (SW 817205). From St Keverne centre a road is signposted to Manacle Point (SW 8121). It presently forks left to Porthoustock, right to Rosenithon (Rosenython). After Rosenithon, the road passes the Giant's Quoits, and then turns sharp left. At the bend, a track leads straight ahead to a gate. Beyond the gate a single-file path skirts a disused quarry to reach the Point. The Point can also be reached by track from Porthoustock. The Giant's Quoits, which once stood on Manacle Point, were resited in 1967 because of quarrying.

St Keyne's Well

About half a mile (1 km) east of the church of St Keyne, in a deep valley, is a well long famous for its power of conferring mastery in marriage to whichever partner drank from it first. It was consequently customary for newly married couples, as soon as they left the church, to dash to the well — but, as Robert Southey says in his ballad *The Well of St Keyne*, the race was not always to the swiftest:

St Keyne's Well.

I hastened as soon as the wedding was o'er
And left my good wife in the porch,
But i'faith she had been wiser than I
For she took a bottle to church.

The well took its name from Keyne, one of fifteen out of 26 children of the fifth-century Welsh king Brechan to become saints. After wandering the country performing miracles, she settled not far from the well. As she was dying, she was carried there on a litter and, desiring peace on earth, gave it its virtue.

Rebuilt in 1976, the well is set in a little garden, sunk beside a lane. Steps lead down to the moss-grown wellhouse, sheltering a square pool. A granite slab nearby tells the legend.

OS 201: SX 247602. ¹/₂ m (1 km) south of St Keyne, 2 miles (4 km) south of Liskeard, on B3254. The well is signposted down a lane to the left, from the church.

St Levan

A cleft stone in St Levan's churchyard, to the left of the porch, has long been an object of wonder. St Levan is said to have been a keen angler who used to sit on the stone when he returned tired from fishing. He decided to leave a memorial of himself in his favourite resting place, so before he died he struck the rock with his fist and split it open. Then he prayed over it and prophesied:

When with panniers astride,
A pack-horse one can ride
Through St Levan's stone,
The world will be done.

As the folklorist Robert Hunt, who had known the stone for more than fifty years, observed in 1881: 'it may be a satisfaction to many to know that the progress of separation is an exceedingly slow one.'

OS 203: SW 3822. 3 miles (5 km) southeast of Land's End, via B3315 to Newlyn and minor road from Trethewey. A footpath opposite the church also leads to the magnificently sited St Levan's Well, SW 382219.

St Madron's Well

A ruinous chapel and a square hole in the ground not far off are all that remains of this once famous healing well near which the Cornish saint Madron or Maderne was buried, though you may still find votive rags and ribbons tied to the bushes, left by modern pilgrims.

Votive rags left in the bushes at St Madron's Well by pilgrims.

A miraculous cure that took place at Madron Well happened in about 1640. Years before, twelve-year-old John Trelille was playing football with friends when a girl hit him on the back with a thick stick for running off with the ball and so injured him that for sixteen years he was forced 'to go creeping on the ground'. Then he dreamed that if he bathed in St Madron's Well or the stream running from it he would be cured. At that time, people used to come to the well on a Thursday in May so, helped by his neighbour, John came on successive Thursdays in May and, after praying in the chapel, washed his body in the stream and lay down on a grassy hillock known as St Madron's Bed. On the third Thursday, he rose quite cured. In 1644 he enlisted in the King's army and was killed shortly afterwards.

The waters of Madron Well were later considered particularly beneficial for children's complaints — 'shingles, tetters and wildfires'. The treatment involved not only immersion in the water, but walking round the well nine times and sleeping on the marshy ground beside it — the cure still required 'incubation' (sleeping near a holy well or shrine) just as it had in John Trelille's day and long before (it was practised in temples of healing in Greek and Roman times).

But gradually the famous healing well dwindled as elsewhere into a mere wishing well. In the 1890s, people would throw in two pins or pebbles 'to try for sweethearts'. If both sank, it was a sign that they would soon be married.

OS 203: SW 445328. Near Madron, 2 miles (3 km) west of Penzance by the minor road to Madron and Trevowhan off A30 (Penzance-Land's End road) at Heamoor. The well is 1 mile (2 km) north-west of Madron, reached along a public footpath beginning just west of the village, and signposted. Madron Well Chapel (SW 447328), AM.

St Mawgan (St Mawgan-in-Pydar)

The churchyard has a remarkable lantern cross of 1420, but its most evocative memorial, shaped like the stern of a boat, records a seafaring tragedy:

HERE LIE THE BODIES OF
JACOB WILLIAMS. DAVID ROBERTS.
OWEN HUGHS. THOMAS COLLINS.
CHARLES CAWLEY. RICHARD CUTLER.
WILLIAM LOYD. WILLIAM ELIOTT.
THOMAS BROWN. JEMMY.
who were drifted on shore in a boat, frozen to death, at Tregurrian Beach in this Parish. on Sunday 13th.Dec.'
MDCCCXLVI.

The nine men and a boy had survived

The stern-shaped memorial at St Mawgan to nine men and a boy who, having been shipwrecked, died as they tried to escape by lifeboat.

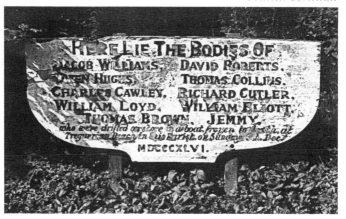

HERE LIE THE BODIES OF
JACOB WILLIAMS, DAVID ROBERTS,
OWEN HUGHS, THOMAS COLLINS,
CHARLES CAWLEY, RICHARD CUTLER,
WILLIAM LOYD, WILLIAM ELIOTT,
THOMAS BROWN, JEMMY
who were drifted on shore in a boat, frozen to death at
Tregurrian Beach in this Parish, on Sunday 5th Dec.
MDCCCXLVI.

shipwreck only to perish wretchedly in their lifeboat.

* * * * *

In 1754 an unidentified ship of 250 tons, on a voyage from Leghorn to Liverpool, was driven ashore on the north Cornwall coast at Mawgan. All the crew survived, and the ship itself remained fairly intact until, according to the *Sherborne Mercury*, 'a parcel of Cornish barbarians from St Agnes, Lower St Columbe, etc., came to the place, and demanded the whole as wreck'. A local magistrate managed to rescue part of the cargo, raw silk to the value of £10,000, but was set on when he ordered guns loaded with powder to be discharged at the mob. The wreckers had their way, and the remaining cargo of cotton, liquorice and oil was carried off and the vessel burnt.

OS 200: SW 8765. 5 miles (7 km) northeast of Newquay via A3059 and minor road. Tregurrian or Watergate Beach (SW 8465), west of B3276 (Newquay-Padstow road) by minor road from St Mawgan to Tegurrian. Cornwall Coast Path.

St Michael's Mount

Originally a monastic site, St Michael's Mount was so called from its mother house, Mont St Michel in France. The name applies well to both,

as St Michael was the saint of high places, because in Christian tradition it was he who cast Lucifer out of heaven.

The great rock, reached by a causeway at low tide, is now surmounted by a fourteenth-century castle. Even before this was built, the site recommended itself as a fortress. During the captivity of Richard the Lionheart in Austria, Hugh de la Pomeroy of Berry Pomeroy Castle in Devon sided with Prince John. On Richard's return, he sent a herald to sound out Hugh's loyalty. The herald soon learned enough for a charge of treason, so Hugh stabbed him to death and fled to Cornwall. He seized St Michael's Mount but soon found himself besieged. As he could not hold out, he had a surgeon open his veins and committed suicide in the Roman fashion.

* * * * *

Of Cornwall's many giants, the giant of St Michael's Mount is the most famous. His name was Cormoran, and he and the giant on Trecrobben Hill were friends. They had only one hammer between them, which they would throw back and forth from one to the other, as needed. One day Cormoran's wife unfortunately ran out of her cave just as Trecrobben threw the hammer and it struck her between the eyes. She fell dead at Cormoran's feet, and he and Trecrobben lifted Chapel Rock and

St Michael's Mount.

buried her beneath it. Trecrobben died of remorse after burying his treasure under Trecrobben Hill (see **Trencrom Hill**) and Jack the Giant-Killer made an end of Cormoran using the same underhand trick employed against the giants of **Mawgan**.

* * * * *

The Cornish name of St Michael's Mount is *Carrick luz en cuz*, 'the ancient rock in the wood', and the fossilised remains of trees can be glimpsed in Mount's Bay at low tide. In the past these gave rise to much speculation, and there was a legend old in Tudor times that spoke of a lost town lying drowned beneath the waves.

OS 203: SW 5129. ¹/₂ mile (1 km) south of Marazion, 3 miles (4 km) east of Penzance, off A394 to Helston. There is access on foot over the causeway at low tide, or, during summer months, by ferry at high tide. National Trust (Castle and Priory).

St Nectan's Glen and Rocky Valley

A few miles inland from Tintagel, a deep valley leads to a waterfall plunging into what is known locally as the Kieve ('basin'). The hermit St Nectan, said to have lived here in the fifth century, when he was dying threw his silver chapel bell into the Kieve. The saint himself, with his church treasure, was buried under the waterfall. When, centuries later, miners tried to blast their way through the Kieve to find St Nectan's treasure, they heard the ringing of a silver bell and a voice saying: 'The child is not yet born who shall recover this treasure.'

The story of St Nectan's treasure became interwoven with the tale of two strange ladies who supposedly at his death took up residence in his oratory. They lived here for years in almost perfect seclusion, and the local people did not even know their names, though they believed them to be sisters. Eventually news somehow reached them that one of the sisters had died. They found the other sitting by the corpse, silent and dry-eyed even when they took it for burial. Days passed, and she did not leave the oratory. At last a child, peeping through the window, saw her still sitting in her chair. She, too, was lifeless. The local people buried the second sister beside the first, but they have no memorial. They were real enough, however: when the novelist Wilkie Collins visited the Glen in 1850, the ladies had been dead only half a century and had no connection with St Nectan.

* * * * *

The stream running through the Glen continues seawards through the narrow gorge of Rocky Valley, a grim cleft of dripping slate, formerly the home of the Cornish chough — a red-billed crow once common in Cornwall and said, like the raven at **Marazion**, to be the reincarnation of King Arthur.

OS 200: SX 0788 and SX 0789. Near Trethevey, 4 miles (6 km) north-west of Camelford, via B3266, then B3263 through Tintagel. Public footpaths lead from the village to St Nectan's Glen, Rocky Valley and St Nectan's Kieve (SX 082886).

St Nonna's Well

St Nonna's Well at Pelynt nestles in a bank above a steep meadow running down to woods which hide the river Trelawne as it flows to join the Looe estuary. The little well-house — no more than a bit of wall, a lintel and an arch — is recessed into the bank and the round stone basin inside catches water trickling from the hillside.

St Nonna's Well.

Though dedicated to St Nonna or St Nun, said to have lived and died at Altarnun, the Pelynt well was thought to be a fairy well. Overshadowed by a great oak, it was known as the Piskies' Well and people threw pins in it 'to get the goodwill of the piskies'. As with other holy wells, it was taboo to destroy it, and local legend tells how a farmer who wanted its basin for a pig trough came to a bad end. He hitched his oxen to the basin and, although for a long time they would not budge, eventually they began to haul it up the hill. Near the top, however, the basin burst its chains and rolled back to its former position. No one has since tried to shift it because from that day on the farmer never prospered.

The great oak, growing through the roof of the well, had shaken down a mass of masonry by the mid nineteenth century, so it was cut down and the well was restored. A young tree must have been planted to take the old one's place, as another oak is growing there today.

OS 201: SX 224564. About 2 miles (3 km) north-east of Pelynt by minor road off the northbound B3359 to Muchlarnick. Before Sowden's Bridge, at the point of a sharp bend, a private road leads off to Hobb Park. The well is signed, with steps down to the path, on the right just after the cattle grid. The path follows the line of the hedge to the wooden-railed enclosure round the well. Signs of changing this access.

St Piran's Oratory

Under the sandhills behind Perran Beach is rumoured to lie the great town of Langarroc or Langarrow. The town grew rich from mining, but with wealth the people became dissolute. So evil were the town's ways that one night a storm arose and buried it and all its people under the sand. Even now, on a stormy night, the bells of seven churches can be heard above the roaring of the sea.

People remembered the story when

in 1835 the shifting sands revealed a small sixth- or seventh-century oratory among the dunes in the parish of Perranzabaloe. In old Cornish the name of this parish means 'the church of St Piran in the sands', and the oratory is believed to have been built on the spot where the missionary saint Piran landed from Ireland. Later the sands enveloped it, though it reappeared in the sixteenth century and again in the nineteenth. Now only a stone marks the spot. A little to the north-east is St Piran's Cross, with gladwyn (*Iris foetidissima*) growing at its foot. This small wheel-headed cross is believed to mark the site of the saint's hermitage and nearby are the scant remains of St Piran's Church.

Piran was a real monk of the Dark Ages, but he is now almost lost in legend. This says that he left Ireland when the Irish got tired of his good deeds and threw him into the sea chained to a millstone. By a miracle he was able to sail on the stone until he reached Cornwall, where he landed on the sands in the district now associated with him.

OS 200: SW 759564. In Penhale Sands, north of Perranporth, reached via B3285 (Perranporth to Goonhavern), then minor road branching left at Tollgate to Mount. Opposite a side road leading off right, to Rose, is a small plaque marking the route to St Piran's Oratory (AM) along a stretch of the Cornwall North Coast Path (³/₄ mile, 1.2 km). The path cuts across the track leading to St Piran's Cross (SW 772565) and Church (SW 769565), just to the north-east, before turning seawards and passing the Oratory. The coast path skirts a military training area: use OS Pathfinder 1352 (Perranporth). St Piran's Oratory, Cross and Church, AM.

St Piran's Cross.

St Ruan's Well

This little well lay at the heart of a mystery. St Ruan or Rumon was one of many Irish saints who came to Cornwall. He built a cell somewhere near the present-day village bearing his name and was buried in his oratory, which became St Rumon's Church. However he was largely forgotten locally when, shortly before AD 960, Ordulph, duke of Cornwall and Devonshire, built a church at Tavistock dedicated to Ruan and translated his relics there.

In the sixteenth century a *Life of St Rumon* was found which suggested that, like other Cornish saints, Ruan settled near a spring, useful both for drinking and for baptism. Speculation led to St Grade's Well, nearly half a mile (1 km) from Grade church, but very near St Ruan. Its water had long been used for all baptisms in the neighbourhood. Antiquaries guessed that Grade was a hermit who later settled by the well, but that it had originally belonged to Ruan.

The *Life of St Rumon* tells that Ruan became a bishop in Cornwall but left to go to Brittany. A curious story is told of him while he was there. The people became convinced that he was a sorcerer who nightly turned into a wolf which carried off their children. One woman denounced him to the local

St Ruan's Well.

St Sampson's Well.

ruler, Gradlo, for having eaten her daughter. The prince could not flout his people's beliefs as foolish nonsense, but cunningly said that his own wolf-hounds should decide the matter. He would expose Ruan to them and, if he were indeed a werwolf, they would tear him to pieces. Everyone was content with this plan. Gradlo secretly let his hounds get to know Ruan and learn to feed from his hands. Consequently, when the monk was put in with the dogs, they came and licked his hands and the people were satisfied he was not a werwolf.

Although St Ruan's Well was altered by restoration in the nineteenth century, visitors remarked that its 'former venerable and picturesque condition' was well preserved. The roof and walls are of roughly shaped stones, massive quoins support a curved arch, and there is a little alcove at the back which perhaps held a statue.

The well-house formerly had a door, as can be seen from the bolt holes, but now it is open to the air. The water in the well, floored with rocks, is about a foot (30 cm) deep, fresh and clear, and even in summer very cold. Cattle drink here, adding to, rather than detracting from, its quiet air of sanctity.

OS 203: SW 714147. At St Ruan, 3 miles (5 km) north of Lizard Point, via A3083 from Lizard. Easiest to spot from a car by taking the third minor road to the right off A3083 (to Ruan Minor), not the first (to Cadgwith). Just before Ruan Minor, a right turn leads to St Ruan; the next right after that leads past the well, also on the right. Its stone roof can just be glimpsed above an overgrown field-wall and steps give on to it. St Rumon's Church, Ruan Major, SW 7016 (AM).

St Sampson-in-Golant

The church of St Sampson-in-Golant, with its little squat square tower and neat walled churchyard overlooking the Fowey estuary, would be worth a visit even without St Sampson's Well, venerated for its association with the Welsh bishop whose hermit's cell stood beside it in the sixth century. It plays a part in the Tristan saga connected with **Castle Dore**.

According to an early version of the story, written in the twelfth century but probably using sources from before the Norman Conquest, Tristan's uncle, King Mark of Cornwall, lived at 'Lancien', probably the medieval manor of Lantyan-in-Golant. At a point in the story when the estranged Iseult is reconciled with King Mark, she rides with his barons to the nearby church of St Sampson, where she makes an offering on the altar of a silken robe embroidered with gold. Afterwards, it was made into a chasuble and kept in the church treasury, only being used on great annual feasts such as Easter and Christmas. 'Those who have seen it', adds the poet telling the story, 'say it is still in St Sampson's'.

OS 200: SX 121551. Near Golant, 2 miles (3 km) north of Fowey, via B3269 (Lostwithiel road). The minor road from Tywardreath to Golant, crossing B3269 at Castle Dore, is signposted to St Sampson's-in-Golant Church before reaching the village. The holy well adjoins the church, left of the porch.

St Teath

Anne Jeffries, born at St Teath in 1626, went into service when she was nineteen with a family called Pitt. She was full of curiosity about fairies and would go out looking for them on moonlit nights singing:

Moon shines bright, waters run clear,
I am here, but where's my fairy dear?

One day in 1645, sitting in the Pitts'

garden, she fell down in a fit. She was ill for some time but on recovering said she had been approached by six tiny men in green. One touched her eyes and she was whirled through the air with a humming sound to a strange and beautiful country. Eventually she was brought back as she had gone and awoke lying on the ground surrounded by an anxious household.

She never returned to fairyland but had many meetings with what she called 'airy people'. From them she learned the art of healing and was famous for her prophecies, but, as she always foretold victory for the King and was 'strangely saucy against the Parliament' during the Civil War, she fell foul of the authorities. She was committed to **Bodmin** Gaol by Tregeagle, later of **Dozmary Pool**, who gave orders for her to be starved, despite which she continued in good health and was eventually released. She afterwards claimed that throughout her imprisonment she had been fed by the 'airy people'.

The churchyard has many slate gravestones and in the church is one dated 1580, thought to be the oldest in the county.

OS 200: SX 0680. 3 miles (5 km) southwest of Camelford, on A39.

A grim warning on one of the slate gravestones at St Teath.

O Reader now who e'er you be,
That read these lines concerning me:
As God can quickly stop your breath
Prepare! prepare for Sudden death

King Arthur's Tomb at Slaughter Bridge.

Seaton Sands

The small beach known as Seaton Sands, between Downderry and Looe, is said to be all that remains of a once prosperous town. Some local sailors are reputed to have insulted a mermaid, who put a curse on it, in consequence of which the sea swept in and buried it under the sand.

OS 201: SX 3054. 3 miles (5 km) east of Looe, via B3253 to Widegates, A387 as far as Hessenford, then B3247 to Seaton.

Sennen Cove

Sennen Cove was once the haunt of the mysterious Whooper, so-called from the whooping sounds it made. It used to foretell storms and would prevent fishermen from leaving the cove when a storm threatened by taking the form of a blanket of mist over the cove in otherwise clear weather.

Then an old fisherman, determined to get to the fishing grounds come what may, persuaded some younger companions to man a boat. Declaring he would not be made a fool of, but would drive the spirit away, he vigorously beat the bank of fog with a threshing flail as they went. The fishermen were never seen again and, as a result of their deed, the mysterious Whooper left Sennen Cove forever.

OS 203: SW 3525. 1¹/₄ miles (2 km) north-east of Land's End via A30 and minor road (west).

Slaughter Bridge

A water-meadow near Slaughter Bridge, on the river Camel, has for centuries been reputed to be the site of King Arthur's last battle, the battle of Camlann. 'For testimony whereof', wrote Richard Carew, in 1602, 'olde folke thereabouts will shew you a stone, bearing *Arthurs* name, though now depraued to *Atry*.'

King Arthur's Tomb is still there, upstream on the bank, a flat stone slab with a worn Latin inscription. Scholars say this is not its original site and the still legible inscription declares it to be the memorial stone, not of Arthur, but of 'Latinus, son of Magarus'. Even Slaughter Bridge does not refer to a slaughter: the name means 'muddy'. That a great battle *had* been fought there was believed by locals in Tudor times to be proved by the fact that people had turned up 'bones and harneys' (armour) in ploughing. However, historians today suggest that these were more likely to be the result of a battle fought in AD 825 against the Cornish by King Alfred's grandfather, Egbert of Wessex.

No matter. Hallowed by generations

of make-believe and wishful thinking, this *is* Camlann.

OS 200: SX 1185. Slaughter Bridge crosses the river Camel 1 mile (2 km) above Camelford. Reached via A39 north to Collan's Cross, then B3314 to Slaughter Bridge. From the driveway beside the bridge, signed Worthyvale, a footpath leads to the river and the stone. King Arthur's Tomb, SX 109856 (AM).

Stratton

Most of Cornwall's giants are legendary, but Stratton is celebrated as the birthplace of a real one, Anthony Payne, 7 feet 6 inches (2.18 metres) tall, who during the Civil War enlisted as a bodyguard to Sir Bevil Grenville (see **Kilkhampton**). When Sir Bevil was killed at the battle of Lansdowne, Payne set up Grenville's sixteen-year-old son beside the standard and shouted 'A Grenville still leads you.' This rallied the Cornishmen to victory.

Payne carried his master's body back home and lived for the rest of his life in the Grenvilles' manor house, now the Tree Inn, at Stratton. When Payne died, the house had to be altered so that his coffin could be got in and out. A tombstone marks his grave in the village churchyard.

OS 190: SS 2306. 15 miles (24 km) north-west of Launceston via B3254 (Kilkhampton road), then A3072.

Table Mên

At the battle of Vellandruchar, Arthur and the Seven Cornish Kings overcame the Danes. Not a Viking escaped and the mill wheel (Vellandruchar) that gave the battle its name turned with blood flowing seawards. Then Arthur and his men worshipped at Sennen Holy Well, before feasting on the huge rock of Table Mên. The Danes have not yet returned to Cornwall and, when they do, Merlin prophesied that an even greater number of kings will gather at the Table Mên to witness their coming. All this will coincide with the ending of the world.

Table Mên, the 'stone table' at Sennen, where this is to happen, is a large stone slab, possibly natural. Whether to wait by it in the year 2000 (the next 'millennium') is the question.

OS 203: SW 359259. About 1 mile (2 km) from Land's End, on A30 (Penzance road). Table Mên is about ¹/₄ mile (0.5 metres) north of the church, in the hamlet of Mayon.

Talland

Legend says that the building of the church at Talland was originally begun inland, at a place called Pulpit. But every night the stones put up during the day were mysteriously moved to their present site near the sea and a voice was heard crying in the darkness:

Tintagel Castle, popularly believed to have been the birthplace of King Arthur.

> If you would my wish fulfil
> Build the church on Talland Hill.

* * * * *

In the early eighteenth century Talland was well known for its vicar Parson Dodge, who held the living from 1713 to 1747. He was a powerful exorcist who was once called in by the parson of Lanreath to deal with a phantom coach with demon coachman and headless horses that haunted his parish. At the mere sight of Dodge, the demon coachman wailed, 'Dodge is come! I must be gone!' and coach and horses vanished.

People were too terrified to go near Talland church at night in case they met Parson Dodge driving evil spirits down Bridle Lane to the sea. Sceptics suggest that Dodge himself put such stories about to make people stay at home at night, because he was in league with the Polperro smugglers.

OS 201: SX 2251. Above Talland Bay, 2 miles (3 km) south-west of Looe, by minor road to Portlooe and Porthallow. Talland church: SW 228516.

Tintagel Castle

According to Welsh legend, Tintagel was the stronghold of King Mark of Cornwall, celebrated in several tales, though today chiefly remembered as the uncle of the hero Tristan (see **Castle Dore**).

At Tintagel itself the Arthur industry is rampant owing to a departure from tradition by Geoffrey of Monmouth (*c*.1136), who set the birth of King Arthur here. According to Geoffrey, while Gorlois, Duke of Cornwall, was away fighting at 'Dimilioc' (perhaps **St Dennis**), Merlin transformed Uther Pendragon, king of the Britons, into the Duke's likeness. Thus disguised, he entered the castle and lay with Ygerne, the Duke's wife, who nine months later bore Arthur.

Long after Geoffrey's time, the romantic appearance of the ruined castle encouraged further embroidery on this story: in one version the baby Arthur is washed up by the waves into Merlin's arms as he stands at the foot of the cliffs. Hollowed rocks near the castle became known as Arthur's Cups and

Towednack parish church before 1870.

Saucers, and a cave below the castle, on the shoreline, as Merlin's Cave.

OS 200: SX 048891. 4 miles (7 km) north-west of Camelford, via northbound A39, then B3314 across **Slaughter Bridge** *to Tintagel village. English Heritage.*

Towednack

At Towednack church the Devil refused to allow completion of the church tower and by night undid what had been done by day. As proof of the tale, the church's squat tower is to this day unadorned by turrets or pinnacles. 'There are no cuckolds in Towednack, because there are no horns on the church tower,' runs a local proverb.

* * * * *

Like the Wise Men of Gotham, the men of Towednack once tried to build a hedge round a cuckoo to preserve eternal spring. 'Penning the cuckoo' is a tale also told at Gorran and **Zennor**. According to another tradition, the Towednack Cuckoo Feast on the Sunday nearest 28th April commemorated the day on which the bird brought spring to Cornwall. One cold and wintry April, a farmer invited his friends to warm themselves at his fire and threw a hollow log on it. To their surprise, a cuckoo flew out of the log and at once the weather became warm and springlike. Towednack is not the only place in England where a local April fair is supposed to mark the first appearance of the cuckoo.

OS 203: SW 4838. 2 miles (4 km) south-west of St Ives, via B3306 (St Just road), and minor road.

Tregagle's Hole

Only the wildest and worst of Cornwall's ghosts, Jan Tregeagle or Tregagle could have carved out this great natural arch from a rocky promontory, enabling the turbulent sea to boil beneath the land. Though he is far from his usual haunts of **Roche Rock** and **Dozmary Pool**, he plays his traditional role of elemental spirit crying above the storm.

OS 204: SX 913377. About ½ mile (1 km) south of **Carne Beacon**. *From the hamlet of Carne (SX 913383) a public footpath is*

signposted to Parador Cove and the link to the coast path. The footpath passes through a gate marked 'Defined footpaths Nos. 44 & 45' and comes to another signpost. The route to Nare Head leads to a T junction. Tregagle's Hole is in a rocky promontory to the left.

Trencrom Hill

Trencrom Hill near Lelant is a gorse-covered hill surmounted by a small iron age hillfort known as Trencrom Castle. Tradition says that giants once lived here who hid their treasure in the hill, where it is guarded by spriggans (something between ghosts and fairies). A man who dug here for the giants' gold was frightened away by a tremendous storm and the arrival of numbers of spriggans looking 'as ugly as if they would eat him'.

Tregagle's Hole.

Trencrom is old Trecrobben, and the Giant of Trecrobben, who plays a part in the legends of **St Michael's Mount**, is one of the giants who lived here. At the foot of Trencrom Hill, beside the Lelant-Towednack road, is a huge granite boulder known as the Bowl Rock. Tradition says that the giants of Trencrom Hill were fond of a game of bowls and as their 'woods' used boulders. The Bowl Rock was one of the woods that rolled to the bottom of the hill and was never recovered.

OS 203: SW 518362. 3 miles (4 km) south of St Ives, via B3311, then minor road to Trencrom and Lelant Downs. The Bowl Rock is beside the road in the village. A public footpath leads from it to the hillfort, crossing the minor road between Lelant Downs and Trencrom Row. National Trust (including Bowl Rock).

Trerice

This magical little manor house, hidden among narrow Cornish lanes, has changed little since it was built in 1573. It replaced an even older house, one of whose owners was Sir John Arundell, who in the reign of Edward IV lived at Efford, on the north coast. He was a magistrate and highly regarded but fell foul of a shepherd believed to possess supernatural powers. This man was imprisoned by Arundell and when he got out of jail took to waylaying him, giving him threatening looks and muttering:

> When upon the yellow sand,
> Thou shalt die by human hand.

Sir John was a brave man, but not foolhardy: he moved from Efford, on the sands, to the wood-clad hills of Trerice, where he lived for several years.

Then Richard de Vere, Earl of Oxford, seized St Michael's Mount and Sir John, as sheriff of Cornwall, tried to retake it. While his forces were encamped on Marazion sands, the Earl's men made a sortie from the castle and Sir John received a mortal wound. At

Trerice.

the moment of his death, the shepherd once more appeared, singing triumphantly:

> When upon the yellow sand,
> Thou shalt die by human hand.

OS 200: SW 8458. 3 miles (5 km) southeast of Newquay via A392 to Quintrell Downs and A3058 towards St Austell, turning right at Kestle Mill. National Trust.

Treryn Dinas

Treryn Dinas is a magnificent headland near **Porthcurno** which during the iron age was made into a cliff castle by the addition of five ramparts. The massive fort shares its Cornish name, roughly speaking, with **Castle-an-Dinas**, Ludgvan, and other places, but not surprisingly it is also known as Giant's Castle.

According to legend, it was built by a giant well versed in the black arts, who sat on the promontory one night and willed the castle to rise from the sea. The key to the castle was an egg-shaped stone, and this he placed in a cavity in the rock locally known as the Giant's Lock. Just before he died, he prophesied that, if anyone moved this stone, both the castle and the promontory would sink beneath the sea. The stone was rumoured in the 1880s still to be there, but along a dangerous ledge and inaccessible.

OS 203: SW 398222. 4 miles (6 km) southeast of Land's End, off B3315 to Newlyn at Treen. Reached by field path from Treen or along the coastal path from Penberth Cove. National Trust. Sometimes called Treen Dinas (not to be confused with Trereen Dinas, near another Treen, 5 miles (8 km) west of St Ives, OS 203: SW 432388).

Trevilley

Trevilley was of old the estate of Treville, given to a family of the name of Vingoe, who came over with the Conqueror. An eerie and mysterious phenomenon is said to have always marked the death of a Vingoe. 'Above the deep caverns in the Treville cliff', runs the tradition, 'rises a cairn. On this, chains of fire were seen ascending and descending, and often accompanied by loud and frightful noises.'

OS 203: SW 3524. ¹/₂ mile (1 km) south of Sennen, off B3315 from Land's End. A public footpath runs from Trevilley to join the South West Coast Path at Zawn Reeth. This leads west across Trevilley Cliff (SW 349239) towards Pordenack Point. The 'cairn' of the tradition is probably the natural outcrop of Carn Boel (SW 348239), but there are also two tumuli on Pordenack Point (SW 346242). AM.

Veryan

Veryan is celebrated for its Round Houses, five whitewashed and thatched cottages with Gothick windows, each of them completely round. On the village outskirts, buildings in the same style form part of the almshouses. They date from the early nineteenth century, but legend now has it that they were built long ago by a parson, one for each of his daughters, and he built them round so that the Devil would find no corners in which to hide.

OS 204: SW 9139. 7 miles (11 km) southwest of Mevagissey by minor road through

Kestle and Tippetts Shop, or by minor road off A3078 from St Austell to St Mawes, just after Ruan High Lanes. A pair of the cottages guards each end of the village.

Warbstow Bury

Warbstow Bury is an iron age hillfort once believed to be the habitation of a giant. He was killed by a tool thrown by the giant of **Launceston** Castle, much as the wife of the giant Cormoran was killed at **St Michael's Mount**. A long mound within the fort has long been known, surprisingly, in view of the legend, as Arthur's Grave. Though no story is attached to it, it is a reminder that in folk belief Arthur was not the king in Camelot of medieval literature but a hero of giant size.

OS 190: SX 202908. At Warbstow, 7 miles (11 km) east of Boscastle, and east of A39 to Newquay via B3262 to Hallworthy, then minor road. Public footpaths lead west off the road opposite the lane to Warbstow church, on to and around the Bury. AM.

The Gothick Round Houses at Veryan.

Zennor

The most famous of Cornwall's mermaids is the Mermaid of Zennor, whose reputed likeness can be seen on a fifteenth-century bench-end in the chancel of Zennor church.

A finely dressed lady used to come every Sunday to church to listen to Matthew Trewhella, the best singer in Zennor, and finally the pair of them disappeared. Some time later, a mermaid hailed a ship off Pendour Cove and asked them to hoist the anchor, as it had landed on her house and she could not reach her husband and children.

Zennor people surmised that this was the lady who had lured Matthew Trewhella away. Though mermaids often lured sailors to their deaths, there was also an old belief that water spirits needed human husbands to give them souls.

Though the bench-end is traditionally said to commemorate the Mermaid of Zennor, it probably gave rise to the tale.

OS 203: SU 4538. 4 miles (7 km) west of St Ives on B3306.

The fifteenth-century bench-end in Zennor church, said to depict the Mermaid of Zennor.

Further reading

Ashe, Geoffrey. *The Landscape of King Arthur.* Webb and Bower, Exeter and London, 1987.

Baring-Gould, S. *A Book of the West: Cornwall.* 1899; reissued 1981.

Béroul. *Tristan.* Translation by Alan Sedrick. Penguin, Harmondsworth, 1970.

Bord, Janet and Colin. *Sacred Waters.* Granada, London, 1985.

Bottrell, William. *Traditions and Hearthside Stories of West Cornwall* (three volumes). Penzance, 1870-80.

Carew, Richard. *The Survey of Cornwall.* London, 1602.

Courtney, M. A. *Cornish Feasts and Folk-Lore.* Penzance, 1890.

Deane, Tony, and Shaw, Tony. *The Folklore of Cornwall.* Batsford, London, 1975.

Du Maurier, Daphne. *Vanishing Cornwall.* Gollancz, London, 1967; Penguin, Harmondsworth, 1972, reprinted 1986.

Du Maurier, Daphne. *Enchanted Cornwall.* Mermaid Books, London, 1992.

Du Maurier, Daphne, and Quiller-Couch, Sir. A. *Castle Dor.* Dent, London, 1962.

Dyer, James. *The Penguin Guide to Prehistoric England and Wales.* Allan Lane, London, 1981.

Geoffrey of Monmouth. *The History of the Kings of Britain.* Translated by Lewis Thorpe. Penguin, Harmondsworth, 1966; reprinted 1980.

Gilbert, Davies. *The Parochial History of Cornwall* (four volumes). London, 1838.

Halliwell, J. O. *Rambles in Western Cornwall.* London, 1861.

Hunt, Robert. *Popular Romances of the West of England.* London, 1881

Larn, Richard and Bridget. *Shipwrecks Around the Lizard.* Tor Mark, Penryn, 1989.

Payne, H. M. Creswell. *The Story of the Parish of Roche.* Newquay, 1948.

'Q' (Quiller-Couch, Sir Arthur). *Dead Man's Rock.* London, 1887.

Quiller-Couch, M. and L. *Ancient and Holy Wells of Cornwall.* London, 1894.

Ravensdale, Jack. *Cornwall.* Edited by Richard Muir. National Trust Histories, Collins, London, 1984.

Shuel, Brian. *The National Trust Guide to Traditional Customs of Britain.* Webb & Bower, Exeter, 1985.

Timbs, John, and Gunn, Alexander. *Abbeys, Castles and Ancient Halls of England and Wales: South.* London, not dated.

Vivian, John. *Tales of the Cornish Smugglers.* Tor Mark, Penryn, 1969; reprinted, 1990.

Vivian, John. *Tales of the Cornish Wreckers.* Tor Mark, Penryn, second edition 1989.

Westwood, Jennifer. *Albion: A Guide to Legendary Britain.* Granada/Grafton, London, 1985; Paladin, Grafton paperback editions, 1987, 1992.

Whitaker, John. *The Ancient Cathedral of Cornwall History Surveyed* (two volumes). London, 1804.

Index

Places and sites mentioned in gazetteer headings are not listed, but alternative names may be included.
Page numbers in italic refer to illustrations.

LADY   BABY   GYPSY   QUEEN   ELEPHANT   MONKEY   TANGERINE

LADY BABY GYPSY QUEEN
ELEPHANT MONKEY TANGERINE

Short stories from *The Hotspur* magazine

St Johns, Healey, Northumberland, 2009

Contents

Jamie Warde-Aldam

Introduction

The stories you'll find in this anthology have been given to *The Hotspur*, the parish magazine of St Johns, Healey.

Some have appeared in the magazine, some are brand new. They have no unifying style and represent no particular attitude to writing. All they have in common is that they come from funny, talented, generous people who write fiction for their own amusement, not for a living.

The title, LADY, BABY, GYPSY, QUEEN, ELEPHANT, MONKEY, TANGERINE comes from my sister Kate, who having eaten eight plums and being in need of some more, felt that repeating TINKER, TAILOR, SOLDIER, SAILOR (and so on) did justice neither to her fruit-eating ambitions, nor to the growing pile of plum stones on the side of her plate.

What does that have to do with these stories?

It's simple really. None of them have reached the light of day through the hands of literary agents or publishing houses. I'm sure they wouldn't be of the slightest interest to the professionals. And that's the point. Amateur storytellers can give just as much pleasure as the usual suspects we're encouraged to spend our money on.

So, a new set of names for you to enjoy, an unprocessed, un-prescribed addition to your bookshelves: fresh plums, damsons, cherries and perhaps the odd peach.

Heck, there's probably a caterpillar somewhere in here too.

Betsy de Lotbiniere

True Tall Tales

You can get stuck in a story.

I was born in a tall city, into a tall family, fond of telling tall tales. We lived on the 13th floor of a tall building overlooking The Park. They refer to their big patch of green as The Park over there. Such is the swagger of the City it eats up specific names, makes you believe each element stands monolithically alone, that only the world that lies before you is real or important. We lived Uptown, high above the tree line, overlooking the Park, opposite The Museum which was surrounded by The Park. The view was as distracting as having the television on all the time. You were often struck dumb by the change of season or light or weather or concerts or fireworks.

For a long time, as a form of life raft, to keep me from drowning in sad events playing out around me, my mind played the following on a loop:

My mother loved show tunes. Whenever she went to a musical on Broadway, she'd always get the record and play the soundtrack over and over again. Which wasn't so bad if the lyrics were interesting and complicated enough—as with Sondheim. But if it was something simple, like Annie, it was awful. Particularly since she could never remember the words later when she tried to sing them in the street to cheer us up.

One day, I opened the door to my big brother visiting from university out west. He was twenty, on his way to becoming a top professional sportsman while floundering over the business degree my father wanted him to get. The struggle with his studies gave him an angry edge women found irresistible. "Where is she?"

"Who?" I had to raise my voice a little over "The Sun'll come out Tomorrow!" He dropped his bags, brushed right past me. "Hello to you."

"Where's Mom?" his face was full of rage. "You know you can hear that shit from the elevator?"

"At the Greek's."

"What? The Greeks?" a Greek family owned the corner shop.

"Yeah. She forgot bananas for your power shakes."

"I'm not listening to that crap my whole weekend home." he shouted over, "*Tomorrow, tomorrow, I love ya, tomorrow*!" marched straight to the French armoire that concealed the sound-system. I was worried. That needle was the sacred idol of our father. You weren't supposed to touch the head directly. We'd had countless lessons on how to lift it using a special lever on the side of the turntable. You had to push down the small, finely weighted handle with a solemnity that would raise the arm without scratching the record. We weren't allowed to touch the machine before the age of 15. I must have been 17 at the time and wouldn't dare go near the machine if either parent was around.

My brother zipped aside the needle, ripped the record out.

"Shit! You've scratched it!" he had a weird devil-gleam in his eyes and marched to the heavy sash window, opened it wide. "What're you going to —" He took a few steps back before moving very quickly forward, his balletic grace in unison with the considerable force of his great long frame twisting, he frisbeed the sucker into the ether. I was screaming, "Nooooooo!".

Now, from that height, and with the razor sharpness of the record, it was a weapon. I, bookish and plump, fearful of heights, was crying and shouting. But he was at that age of restless limitlessness, grinning, shaking his head, waiting for my squall to finish.

"So little faith, man. So little faith!" He swept his arm out full length like a circus ring-leader inviting me to see for myself. I, risking the stomach swoop of vertigo, stuck my head out the window. My knees almost buckled with relief to hear the usual carnival rumble from the Museum. No screams. Not yet anyway. But the victim could have been a loner, undiscovered. My eyes darted everywhere, looking for a pool of blood. Then, there it was, a flash of dark gleam.

Annie, at the hand of my murderously angry, athletic brother, had flown across Fifth Avenue, over the long flight of tourist-filled steps, beyond the massive fluted columns it had veered right, gone beyond flag pole and fountain, to the flat roof of the Metropolitan Museum of Art without shattering.

And that was the last time I saw him whole. His motorcycle crashed. He smashed his skull into five pieces. Broke his hip and arm and foot. It took him a long time to speak, to remember how to walk, for his short-term memory to improve. It never did come back fully. He was never the same.

I kept telling the story of the unbroken record by way of explaining his former balance and grace, to keep alive the old version of him. I told it so I wouldn't have to talk about what had happened because then I'd get lost in the limitless details of our despair.

We lived there another few years. In that time, there were many lulls in cocktail chat or times you didn't want to look at a screaming parent, disappointed with you or moments when I just plain missed the former version of him. I'd look out for his round, flat black circle with the red ring in the centre sitting amongst the tar and gravel and sometimes weep for his lost prowess.

When we heard there were plans to build a sculpture garden on the roof of the Museum, my sister and I were worried they'd rip up the area where Annie lay. But it was built in the left-hand corner and in the back. I'd catch her standing, looking at the view and ask: "still there?" The red in the centre faded, paper grew thinner, it was harder to find. "Yep," she said five years later on the day the movers came. I stopped telling the story after the context was lost.

I moved to Rome in part to get away from the sadness of my family, in part because I thought I was in love. I married the man, moved to London and after a very long time we divorced. And in order not to get stuck in the canyon of grief, another tale of height and beaten odds came to save me.

It was tough at first, rattling around with my children in a big house I couldn't afford to keep going. So I took on my first lodger. I had only met her once. She was a very tall poet in her early thirties who professed to have a broken heart. She carried the maiden name of my paternal grandmother. All auguring well. I liked her instantly but my instincts were direly rattled after discovering my husband had been cheating for ten years. So we made a date to meet for the second time at a pub. I was screwing myself up to be adult and ask for references.

She said she was six foot two. A tall woman does strange things to the scale of a room. Armchairs are dwarfed, tables shortened, doorways become narrow. I couldn't help staring to see how a pint glass would look like a child's cup as it disappeared into her long spindly hand.

It was a new moon that night. A Sikh friend had told me that you could make a wish on the dark moon. To them, black is the colour of all possibilities. (Such details can save you when you're in the state of crying over every love song on the radio.) All you had to do was write down your heart's desire then light the paper and drop the burning wish in some liquid.

If you then drank the liquid, your wish would come true. So as an ice-breaker I proposed this and—being Irish—she was game. Of course we had Guinness. What else would taste good with charred wishes in it? My wishes were for the hearts of my children to fully mend as soon as possible after the rift with their father. He was the only man I'd ever slept with. A man who, after years of inexplicable, callous behaviour, missing hours and sparks of rage, I finally asked to move out. It was shocking to us all when he moved in with his mistress of ten years' standing.

So another tall story came to save me:

On the dark moon night of wishes, this tall Irishwoman was more definitive in her Cosmic Ordering. She wished for a man over six foot five, dark haired, kind and artistic to fall in love with her. I laughed at her foolhardy waste of an opportunity and pointed out, "Not many men on the planet over six foot five!" In the street she and I were laughing, cajoling, cheering each other on to think of a brighter future. I decided right then to let her the room. She broke into song: "tomorrow! Tomorrow! I love ya tomorrow!" It was the first time in a long time I'd thought of the earlier version of my brother.

It was like having a big yellow cat in the house. She was respectful of our privacy to the point of stealth and so warm and smart when asked to join in with our mini-family we all loved her. A month after she moved in, she stayed out all night. I got a guilty sounding giggling call from her at the office. She'd met an artist. He was dark haired. Was he kind? " A dote," she said. Height? "He's six foot eight!"

By Christmas she was engaged. August we drove to their wedding in Cavan, near the Northern Irish boarder. It's an old car without a stereo and when we sang together, driving off the ferry into Dublin I knew my children would be all right and my wish had come true. At the altar, she looked up at him when she said "I do!" Her very tall child will be born next month.

My brother who is mentally stuck in his twenties never married. He teaches tennis at a nudist colony in Palm Springs. He doesn't remember the record story. He is still tall.

Jamie Warde-Aldam

Dazzled

I adjust my wife's electric bed so that she's facing the garden window. Since her collapse, she's been as helpless as a small baby.

The doctors make optimistic hints about physiotherapy and recovery statistics. I am, however, the only person who knows the reason for this massive insult to her cognitive faculties. And their hope, if it is such a thing, is entirely misplaced.

I put a travel rug over her knees and reflect that she's the second victim of an invention created by a member of my family.

Its first casualty was Lance Cunningham, an able seaman in the Royal Navy. In 1916, having lost a leg in the Battle of Jutland, he was assigned permanent shore duty and attached as an assistant to Captain Norman Wilkinson's naval camouflage division. Wilkinson, an artist in civilian life, invented a camouflage for ships called 'dazzle painting'. Visually arresting to the point of being mesmeric[1], dazzle was influenced by patterns in Vorticist paintings and publications. For those of you unfamiliar with it, the following picture-shorthand may help: *Naval vessel. Large herd of super-size zebras. Collision.*

The popular understanding of camouflage is that it's about concealment. But dazzle doesn't so much own up to its presence as declare war on your senses of proportion and logic. Its intersecting planes, shades and angles break up a ship's mass and, for a U-Boat Kapitan squinting through a periscope, this would present a number of problems. Is the vessel approaching, sailing away or at anchor? Which bit of it is which? Targeting its most vulnerable or explosive parts would have been a nightmare of guesswork. In the days before sonar and long-range aircraft, dazzle was avant-garde in tactical as well as artistic terms.

My great uncle, Stephen Curtis, was also under Wilkinson's command. A graduate of the Slade school of Art, he had become intoxicated by the Vorticists and their charismatic leader,

---

1. Taken from *Uncomfortable Images in Art and Nature*, by Dominic Fernandez and Arnold J Wilkins, Department of Psychology, University of Essex, Colchester.
Our investigation was prompted by concern over the complaints with which contemporary art is sometimes associated. In 1971 when an exhibition of Op art was held in London, the Daily Telegraph reported that the guards complained of headaches and were issued with dark glasses. In 1989, the front page of the Observer carried the story of a newspaper advert with swirling stripes that had been banned after it evoked seizures. In 2005, when a London hospital commissioned artwork and three members of staff complained of migraines in consequence, the resulting controversy reached the national press. An aversive reaction is common in response to the work of many contemporary artists (Haysom 2003; Woolls 2003), including Debbie Ayles who uses her migraines as an inspiration for her art (Podoll 1998).

Wyndham Lewis. Vorticism, like Futurism in Italy, glorified brute modernity, dynamism and warfare. Its machine-age iconoclasm represented a perfect focus for my uncle's youthful aggression. His posting to a row of damp huts on the Liverpool quayside left him weak with fury at his failure to get himself into a front-line ship. As time went on, the sulk lifted and he appeared to relax into the role of *camoufleur* under Wilkinson's watchful eye. But what his commanding officer didn't at first detect was Curtis' desire to align murderous thoughts with a belief in the power of art.

Day after day he applied his compositional and colouration skills to the elevation plans of cruisers, destroyers and merchantmen. Naturally, the more forward-thinking artist-turned-sailors sought to outdo each other in producing striking, provocative arrangements of form and colour to reflect the modern world. In many cases, out-foxing the Hun was a secondary consideration. These ships were, after all, the largest canvases any of them would ever work with, and the challenge to create something new and original was hardly discouraged by their skipper.

Before the first world war, Henri Gaudier-Breszka, a French fellow-traveller of the Vorticists, made a series of small, geometrically simplified animal sculptures. Many of those in the know assumed they had a double purpose as knuckledusters, coshes or eye-gougers. Perhaps this combination of art and weaponry was the spark for my angry relative. At some point during his time in Liverpool, he began work on a dazzle camouflage pattern that was different from the others. One that was so confusing, so unbearably hard for the brain to process that he hoped it would cause irreversible brain damage. These days, we might describe the effect he was looking for as a massive migraine attack, which would cause instant cell death in critical brain areas[2]. Stephen, however, was almost entirely ignorant of science and medicine, possessing instead a deeply troubled, if inventive, mind powered by a surfeit of patriotically-flavoured male hormone.

In his immature imaginings, the invention would save thousands of British lives. Highly-trained enemy crews would be turned into uncontrollable rabbles of incapacitated, mindless men. Needless to say, he failed to factor in the allied crews, dockworkers and Fleet Reviews that his dazzle ships would sail past too.

By spring 1917, he had a design he felt he could put to the test.

Naturally, he had never seen the whole thing as a complete piece. To do so would be a terrible own goal for King, Country and, so he thought, his family. However, Cunningham, with his indolent, one-legged shuffle and cigarette breaks when Stephen needed him most, seemed expendable.

In his diary my uncle wrote of the meticulous planning of what he called 'The Experiment'. Having persuaded the able seaman to stay late to help him finish an urgently needed camouflage, he sent him over to Store Room C for more nibs. To find anything in this dark space required lights and Stephen, with some difficulty, had pinned up the design directly

2. Some types of high-contrast patterned art are known to set off migraines. Migraines, in turn, can lead to small lacunae in brain matter. An image of sufficient power can precipitate an attack of such severity that substantial brain damage occurs within seconds.

opposite the door, at right angles to the light switch. The dazzle pattern was the first thing Cunningham would see.

When he heard the scream, my uncle calmly walked the eighty feet to the store. Before he entered, he tied a black cloth around his eyes and, working from well-rehearsed memory, removed the sheet of paper from the wall. Having rolled it up, he pulled the cloth from his face and studied the result of his experiment. Parts of Lance Cunningham's brain were now riddled with lacunae or small holes, leaving its owner vacant of thought, glassy-eyed and dribbling blood. Uncle Stephen coldly recited the standard test for cognitive function following head injury. Poor Lance, although conscious in a manner of speaking, was clearly unable to understand a word he said, or indeed anything else about the planet he'd been born on. He was worse than dead, wrote Stephen, incapable of fighting and a drain on national resources. The Experiment had worked.

No-one could possibly have guessed what happened that night. Cunningham was assumed to have suffered a massive stroke and having become immobile, incoherent and incontinent, spent the remainder of his unfortunate life in an institution on the Wirral.

My uncle realised, rather belatedly, that he couldn't announce his secret weapon in anything but theoretical terms without being accused of grievous bodily harm, attempted murder or plain madness.

He did, however, introduce the idea to Wilkinson in the mess one evening. The Old Man, suspecting perhaps that might be something more to his excited talk than theory, quietly made arrangements for the young psychopath to be transferred.

Uncle Stephen's life ended not long afterwards in Malta, murdered by the father of an underage girl he'd interfered with. When my father died in the 1970s, I inherited Stephen's sea chest. Dad had rather dismissively mentioned the dazzle business to me once or twice, so I had a sketchy idea of what to expect.

I opened the chest the day after the funeral. There was his diary, which described the invention and the Cunningham Experiment. And beside it, rolled tightly into a metal tube, was the design itself.

Well it was impossible not to take a miniscule look. In fact, it was more or less an involuntary action for me.

With a squirt of adrenalin and a reckless tremor in my hands, I rolled back an inked area of about two square inches. I saw a pattern in blacks, blues and greys that was so obtuse, so intricately contrary in its logic and yet so blindingly gorgeous that I had to look away. A few seconds later, I was on the floor, my head in my hands, with a headache ten times the strength of the most vicious hangover.

There was a quality about it though, a split second of roaring, blissful abandon before the pain came, that persuaded me to look again a few days later.

Inch by inch, I acclimatised myself to its strange illogic, the violent shock and headaches ceding to longer periods of strange, sensual pleasure. Each fragment I allowed myself to look at was so absurdly complicated and beautiful. Never, in a life devoted to looking at great works of art, had I felt so ravished by such an irresistible pattern. And there was another thing. When I was away for more than a day, I felt out of sorts, fogged in the head and vacant. I was becoming dependant on it.

You know what's going to happen now, up to a point.

So I won't trouble you with my descent into addiction (and that's what it is) to the dazzle. Except to say that this part of my story is one of a kind, repeated with a million little personal inflections on station bookstalls the world over. Even my finances mirror those sorry confessions. I stopped going to work so I could spend more time with the dazzle (blah blah). My picture dealing business collapsed (surprise, surprise) and so did my wife Alice, when she finally got to see Uncle Stephen's creation. I'd built myself up to tolerating three quarters of the whole image by then, but for her, it was like falling off a cliff. With the lazy fatalism of the fiend I've become, I knew it was inevitable. Alice's bright, observant mind must have been firing off question marks about me day and night. One windy summer afternoon, she burst in on my study, where I lay in a dazzled reverie, took one look at the terrible vision and succumbed in a folding heap of baffled moans.

With her new disability allowance (rather good news as a matter of fact) and social security, we're considerably better off than we've been for a while. Neither of us eats much and my early parenting skills have fallen back into place. This at least ensures that I don't spend *all* my time dazzling. I'm very conscious of the need for a bit of variety sometimes, even if that does involve inventing slightly strained conversations for us when we're together.

Everything's great actually, apart from my being a hypochondriac about holes in my brain.

Oh, and the whimpering, I can't abide her constant whimpering.

I wonder, if I showed her the dazzle again, do you think she'd shut up?

Karl McManus

Charlie is my Darling

Twas on a Monday morning,
Right early in the year,
When Charlie came to our town
The Young Star Gardener.

(Chorus)
Charlie is my darling, my darling, my darling.
Charlie is my darling, the young star gardener.

This is true. I was a young, lost kid in Hexham. Like so many others with no direction. I hung around with my mates, did a bit of glue 'n spliff. Playstation. But my life had no real meaning. I wasn't going anywhere fast. Not even to Corbridge.

Gardens were nothing to me. Just a patch of earth the dog did his thing on. When we were kids we didn't even have a daffodil. My parents didn't care about the natural world.

Then one day in July two years ago for a joke a few of us went along to a village fete and Charlie Dimmock was there doing a promotion. She was there in her loose jumper and her cords. With her hair. That hair. And I saw what was underneath her nails: Mother Earth. She lit my gardening fire. And the flame is still on like the one under a Burger King Grill.

Charlie is the Top Celebrity Gardener. No contest. But she's far deeper than all the others. She is so natural. Titchmarsh? What a joke. And he writes those dirty books. And Dermot Gavin? I know where I'd plant him. In his concrete. Monty Don? Don't make me laugh.

What was it in Charlie that did it for me? Probably her passion for water features, hardy annuals, her support for wheelchair friendly design, her love of reclaimed sleepers and adoration of quality decking. The way she says "Trachelospermum jasminoides." Charlie is a natural woman. Not like the other girls I know in Hexham. Or elsewhere.

Anyway I went off and got myself together and got an HND-accredited Level Two qualification in Horticultural Studies at Hartlepool College. It was tough. Very tough. There was a lot of practical work. They say I have dospraxia but Charlie kept up my belief through to the end and I passed with 38%.

I think the feelings that a lot of us feel for Charlie is summed up by her fansite on which Chris P wrote:

"Oh that Botticelli Radio Times front cover! All the beauty of my former loves combined pale against the radiance of Charlie. Those tumbling locks of burnt sun falling against a skin creamy smooth and smile demure above and beyond the Mona Lisa. My heart cannot be still nor my soul rest for beauty such as this is more than any mere mortal may bear. My heart cries out with joy for the sight of Charlie ringed about only by garlands."

That is poetry, that is.

I heard some guy describe Charlie as "yokel crumpet." That is so nasty. It is more than just a physical thing with Charlie. As Elton John wrote (and sang) so preciently in 'Candle in the Wind': "Goodbye Norma Jean/ From the young man in the twenty-second row, / Who saw you as something more than sexual. More than just our Marilyn Monroe."

Except Charlie, is of course, unlike Marilyn, still with us. Thank God.

Norman Baker

Northumbria Hospital

First night. 2.00am. No booze so no sleep. In the dark I hear the rattle of a trolley coming towards my bay.

Even at this early stage, various tests need to be made. Blood pressure is high. Temperature is high. Little do they know that this is more to do with the tremens than the accident itself. I take the chance to grab a drink of water before a little electronic probe is inserted in my ear.

"I just need to shine this pencil torch into your eyes Norman. Look straight ahead and try not to blink".

After this comes the most mundane of questions, neurologically based I assume.

"Do you know where you are Norman?" she asks.

"Of course I do Nurse."

"Where are you?"

"I'm in bed."

Encounter with the staff nurse

Monday morning is a frenzy, Linen is changed, breakfast dispensed, pajamas swapped, rounds made. When the dust settles the staff nurse makes herself known. Although not on the same level as Hattie Jacques in the intimidation stakes she is nevertheless clearly in charge. I'm given the what's what and the where while she unceremoniously sticks a plastic junction into the crook of my good arm. This opens the channels for blood, morphine, nutritional supplements or whatever else maybe needed come the time. Unfortunately there isn't a nozzle for vodka.

After she leaves I turn to Malcolm in the next bed.

"She seems alright."

"I don't know about that son."

"What do you mean?"

"The last bloke in here rubbed her up the wrong way."

"What happened?"

"She put a clothes peg in his urine bottle while he was asleep. You could hear the yelps right down the passage."

Encounter with the dinner lady

In his later years my grandfather lived in a nursing home and taught me the importance of these women.

"Keep them sweet son."

A box of Black Magic a month ensured an extra rasher on his plate and a cup of hot sweet rosy at the wave of a hand. I try his approach.

"That sweet was lovely pet."

"You'd pay a fiver down the town for a three courser like that flower."

The results are swift. Tuesday's pasta bake would have kept Jake La Motta quiet and Wednesday morning's bowl of grapefruit had enough Vitamin C in it to cure the crew of the Narcissus. I can just see them in the kitchen.

"What a canny lad that Norman is."

Success on a plate.

Encounter with the pain nurse

Thursday morning and it's clear by now that the codeine/paracetamol combination isn't having any effect on a seasoned DD cabinet like me. Something called Tramadol is mentioned. I nod approvingly and sure enough, a Scottish woman in a district nurse outfit arrives at the bottom of the bed later that day. She has a badge that reads NANCY ALEXANDER. PAIN NURSE. We discuss the accident and I show her the bruise, which by now is a mixture of jaundice yellow and black eye blue. She decides that some stronger stuff is in order and sets about determining the level of my discomfort in order to gauge the dosage.

"On a scale of zero to five, if zero is no pain and five is very sore, which one are you?"

"What number's agony Nancy?"

Encounter with the junior doctor

The day after the all-important CT scan, a coltish young quack pays a visit to bring me up to speed. He talks about little metal plates, knitting of bones and even mentions some new innovation called the polaris nail which sounds quite groovy.

When the shoulder business is concluded, he moves onto the head, which also took a bit of a bashing.

"How was it?"

"Not too bad. Although I've got a bit of a problem with my right ear."

"Oh yes?"

"It's nothing that a piece of sticky tape can't fix."

"You've lost me there Norman."

"Well the other day a friend of mine brought up a Sony Walkman to help relieve the boredom. The left earpiece fits like a glove bit the other one keeps falling out. Don't worry doc, I'll get it sorted."

Adam Douglas

The Thief

When he arrived at the bus stop and took his place among the jostling schoolchildren,
Sebastian reached into his duffle coat pocket and discovered that it had happened again. The
three pennies his mother gave him each day for his bus fare home were gone.

Sebastian scrabbled his fingers into the corners of the deep square pockets, clutching and
scraping at every furred seam, hoping to feel at any moment the reassuring weight of the
jingling copper coins. But they were gone.

He looked around blindly for a moment, wondering whether he could have dropped
them, but rejected the idea just as quickly. He would have heard them as they clattered to the
ground.

There was no use going back inside the school. His coat had been on its hook in the cloakroom all day, and he had donned it quite normally, without tipping or twirling it. And even if he did find the money, the next bus was not for an hour. Such a wait was quite beyond his seven-year-old's powers of endurance.

He simply could not understand how the money had disappeared, or why.

The enormity of the blow, repeated for the third time in as many weeks, robbed him of volition, and all the exhaustion of a long day at school flooded his defences. The yearning to be safe at home with his mother struck him in the belly like a hunger pang. He sagged in defeat, arms dangling by his sides, as he watched the single-decker bus jouncing to a halt alongside the crowded bus shelter.

"Come on, Seb," his kid sister Nessa called to him, as she climbed up in a conger of friends, but he could only gesture helplessly and call to her across the throng.

"It's happened again."

She pulled a sympathetic face, but he knew there was nothing she could do.

He watched as she skipped along the aisle of the bus, briefly keeping eye contact with him but unable to fend off her laughing, chattering friends. By the time the bus was creaking off in a cloud of diesel fumes, she was on the back seat, giggling and gossiping with the rest of them. Sebastian gazed after her fast-receding head, hating her for a moment and hating all the children who rode home on plush seats, while he would have to walk.

The noise and haze of the bus died away and Sebastian was alone at the bus stop.

Elsewhere the world went on, oblivious to his tragedy. On the opposite pavement a woman in a headscarf and coat, handbag on arm, marched her border collie briskly away from him. A single driver in a Ford Prefect coasted past and up the hill after the bus, flicking an incurious glance at Sebastian as he went. The traffic lights at the edge of the village turned amber, then red, amber again, and back to green, but no more vehicles came. The woman and her dog disappeared down a distant garden path.

All was quiet, until, sauntering round the corner from the school gate, with the casual air of a boy who never had the need to hurry to catch the bus, came Jimmy Feather.

"Missed the bus, Seb?"

"I've lost my fare again," Sebastian croaked, his eyes prickling as he gave voice to the terrible injustice.

"Too bad," said Jimmy. He paused, as if he had half a mind to stand at the bus stop and gaze at the empty road for as long as it pleased him to do so, then spat into the gutter with aplomb. "You walking?"

"I'll have to."

"I'm going your way. We'll walk together."

Jimmy didn't wait for an answer but headed off along the pavement towards the hill.

Reluctantly Sebastian trudged after him, though the offer of Jimmy's companionship gave him the tiniest fillip.

The two boys walked together up the steep hill away from the school, past the small green where Sebastian had got a bloody nose in a fight with Brian Armstrong.

Although they had virtually nothing in common, Sebastian liked Jimmy. He liked his mop of dirty blond curls, his half-oriental eyes that disappeared into crinkles when something amused him, his skinny bowed shoulders inside his ever-present green jumper with its frayed sleeves— all attributes quite unlike his own, he with his neat fringe and new duffle coat.

Most of all he liked that Jimmy never threatened him like some of the other poorer kids did. Brian Armstrong who lived in a cul-de-sac opposite the power station had told everyone he wanted to smash Sebastian's face in before Sebastian had even laid eyes on him. His first term, Martin Ryan or one of the others had come running up in the playground, shouting that Brian Armstrong was going to smash his face in, and that he had to meet him after school.

The rest of the day had been an endless agony of butterflies-in-the-stomach for Sebastian, though the fight when it finally came had been neither long nor memorable. His bloodied nose was a kind of defeat in Sebastian's opinion, but he had inflicted a few blows himself without quite knowing how and was still standing at the end of it, and the other boys seemed to regard the trickle of blood as a badge of honour.

Brian Armstrong had left him alone after that, but he still uttered occasional threats which Martin Ryan and his crew delighted in relaying to Sebastian, goading him to be scared, cheekily offering to hold his coat. Sebastian was scared all right, but he couldn't show anybody that. He just kept out of Brian Armstrong's way, and miraculously Brian Armstrong kept out of his.

Jimmy was nothing like that. He was sometimes in fights himself of course, though never with Sebastian. He was not one of Sebastian's best friends—Stephen Heslop and Mark Robson were that—and he was strangely elusive at school, quiet in the classroom and isolated in the playground, whereas Sebastian was inclined to be boisterous in class, exulting in knowing more of the answers than most to the questions asked by the teachers. But Jimmy didn't hold that against Sebastian, and he had been one of the first to clap Sebastian on the back after the fight and reassure him that he done well. Sebastian had been grateful for that, though he would have been more grateful if Jimmy could have thought up some way of postponing the fight altogether.

Sebastian felt his shins begin to ache as he climbed the steep hill, struggling a little to keep up with Jimmy. He was exhausted already as they breasted the slope and headed along the undulating road that led the mile or so to their home village.

Jimmy lived in the low-rise estate further along the main road, almost opposite the turning at the foot of Sebastian's leafy street. Sebastian's mother had said that those were blocks of flats, though Sebastian had no clear or fixed idea what that meant. In his self-pity Sebastian thought ahead to the moment when Jimmy would vault the low brick wall and head towards one of the squat concrete boxes, where presumably his tea was waiting for him, leaving Sebastian to walk alone and hungry up his own street, the last task of his journey being to surmount the second of the two hills that made walking home such an exhausting chore.

But at least the first hill was negotiated.

"Can we slow down?" Sebastian panted, unhooking the toggles of his duffle coat to flap the autumnal breeze onto his heaving chest.

"Yeah, sure," Jimmy agreed, slowing his pace to fall into step with him.

They walked on in silence, Jimmy occasionally gnawing meditatively at the sleeve of his jumper. The small parade of shops they passed—a newsagent's, a launderette, an off-licence—were succeeded by houses, then the long graveyard wall and the grey bulk of the Presbyterian church, then fences and hedges and nothing in particular, as they reached the limits of the village in which their school stood.

"How did you do in the spelling test?" Sebastian asked, thinking back to his chief triumph of the school day.

"What? Oh, that. Didn't do it."

"Why not?"

"Didn't know there was one." Jimmy shrugged, unconcerned.

"How could you not know?"

"Wasn't at school yesterday, was I?"

Sebastian was baffled for a moment, then realised, with a little squeeze of guilt, that he had not even noticed Jimmy's absence.

"Where were you?"

"Playing hookie, like."

"What's that?"

"Are you kidding us?" Jimmy immediately realized that Sebastian was sincere. It was like him not to take the opportunity to mock. "You know, playing truant."

"Oh." Sebastian thought this through. He knew what truant was, but primarily from schoolboy fiction. He tried to put himself in Jimmy's shoes, surviving a whole eight hours while evading discovery. The effort defeated him. "What did you do all day?"

"You know, this and that. Enjoyed myself."

"What did you have for lunch?"

"Didn't bother."

"Weren't you hungry? Didn't your parents notice?"

"Mam's working all day."

"What about your dad?"

"He's away."

Sebastian remembered that Jimmy had told him this before. "Still?"

"He's away a long time."

"Your brother's away as well, isn't he?"

"Aye, well, one is. The other's in the army."

Having only a younger sister, Sebastian had sometimes fantasised about an older brother, someone to take him fishing or play football with him or scare off the likes of Brian Armstrong. "You must miss them."

"Not them bastards." For a second Jimmy's shoulders hunched even further forward, then he perked up. "Hey, let's play knocky-nine-doors."

"No," Sebastian said quickly, "let's not."

Knocky-nine-doors was the name Jimmy gave to the game of ringing on stranger's doorbells and running away. He had explained it to Sebastian the last time they had walked home together, and Sebastian had known immediately that this was a game he never wanted to play.

Ahead of them was a terrace of four small red-brick houses. This was where Jimmy had last proposed playing the game, though Sebastian had managed to forestall him by asking deliberately obtuse questions about the rules, or at least pretending to think that there must be something more to them than the simple imperative of causing a nuisance.

"No, we will," Jimmy said. "I'll do the first one if you're scared."

Sebastian had been bracing himself for an accusation of being chicken, and briefly registered that Jimmy at least eschewed that loaded word. He wanted to please Jimmy, of course, but his whole soul revolted against the notion of playing the game. Once more the familiar terror screwed through his innards, and he hated his fear, wondering if there would ever dawn a school day when he wasn't scared at least once.

He had no idea who lived in these houses, but the image of their inhabitants, perhaps rough ex-miners or off-duty policemen, rushing out to seize him by the arm filled him with dread. Those short front paths suddenly seemed to stretch out before him like the hundred-yard dash marked out on the field for sports day—and he had never been much good at running.

"It's not that," he muttered.

"What then?"

Jimmy had stopped altogether now, and Sebastian struggled to think of a way to get him moving again. He yearned to get away from these houses, whose inhabitants might already be sizing them up through the net curtains.

"What's the point?" he asked.

"It's fun."

Sebastian said nothing.

"I tell you what," Jimmy said. "We'll play the game, then I'll get us some sweets."

Fifty yards further down the road was a small paper shop. The last time they had walked together, Jimmy had gone in there and emerged with a Batman pack of chewing gum and, unbelievably, had torn the single stick of gum in two and given half to Sebastian, and let him keep two of the three cards. It was a special bond between them, because no-one else in the world, not even Stephen Heslop or Mark Robson, ever shared their sweets. And chewing gum had a particular allure, as Sebastian's parents strictly forbade him to eat it. He kept the two cards—one of Robin punching two of the Penguin's goons at once (with a big starburst pow!), the other of the Batmobile—in his bedside cupboard and looked at them again and again.

Sebastian shivered with nerves at the foot of the first garden path. He had hoped that a gate might offer him the excuse of an immovably rusted latch, but these houses had no gates.

He felt a multitude of angry eyes boring into him from all the windows.

He took a single step forward.

"Don't hang around," Jimmy advised him.

Sebastian took another step, then another. Somehow, without having consciously decided to get there, he was at the front door of the first house, hugging it close to avoid being seen from the small bay window. He was standing so near that he could see individual brush strokes in the gloss paint.

Jimmy stood grinning at the foot of the path, seemingly a thousand miles away, and braced for flight. "Go on," he urged.

Sebastian listened for a moment, hoping that the house was empty, and heard nothing. Then panicking, he frantically rapped at the door, once, twice, three times, much louder than he had intended, bruising his knuckles.

Instantly an old woman's voice cried out in a terrified quaver from the back of the house, and he heard in its echo the poverty and thinness of its few rooms.

"What is it? What do you want? Can't you leave me alone?"

As though she knew him instantly and had endured a thousand times or more his malevolent knocking.

A fierce blast of shame scorched through him in that split-second as he registered all her fear and bewilderment, and then he fled back down the path, leapt out onto the pavement and sprinted after Jimmy, who was racing ahead of him, his blond curls streaming behind like a banner, laughing with delirious glee.

They came to a lung-bursting halt outside the paper shop. Sebastian's cheeks flamed and his heart thumped. He massaged his stinging knuckles.

Jimmy was still laughing. For the second time that afternoon Sebastian felt hot tears welling up.

"It wasn't funny, Jimmy," he protested.

"It was brilliant, man."

"But you're usually so kind."

The compliment hung in the air like an accusation.

Jimmy shook his mop of hair and rubbed his eyes. "Oh well," he said. "I'll get us some sweets."

"How will you do that?" Sebastian said. "Have you got any money?"

"I've got a bit," Jimmy said, fishing in his pocket, and Sebastian had a brief glimpse of three pennies clutched in his grubby hand.

Sebastian did not go in with Jimmy but waited nervously outside the shop, glancing back down the street to the poor old woman's house. No avenging son or burly neighbour materialized to take up her cause.

The shop door clattered shut and Jimmy slapped a pack of Batman gum into his hand. "You like Batman, don't you? There you go." He had a second packet in his hand. "I got the Monkees."

At once Sebastian's faith in Jimmy was restored. A whole packet all to himself. A whole piece of gum and three cards. Unimaginable riches.

The two boys walked on together, Sebastian inching the cardboard sliver of gum into his mouth and savouring its first minty surge.

They compared cards as they chewed and walked. Jimmy let him swap the Batmobile card he already had for one of the Monkees riding funny little motorbikes round their living room.

Now that the adrenaline had subsided, Sebastian felt shaky and tired, but he saw with surprise that they had covered most of the mile and were approaching the turning to his road. The low brick wall to Jimmy's estate was in sight on their left.

He glanced down at the wrapper of his Batman gum.

"How did you buy two packets?"

"Eh?"

"You only had thrupence, didn't you? These are thrupence each."

"I nicked one."

"But Jimmy … that's stealing."

Jimmy shrugged. "I paid for one, slipped the other in my pocket. That old gadgie never noticed. One for each of us. See you tomorrow."

And, as Sebastian had foreseen, Jimmy hopped over the wall and strolled away across the rough grass towards his block of flats.

"Who do you want to invite to your birthday party?" his mother asked.

It was the first really warm day of summer, and they sat at the garden table under the shade of the tall elm while Nessa and her new friend Femi rose higher and higher on the swings. Sebastian had been told many times how lucky he was to have a June birthday.

Sebastian reeled off the names almost without thinking. Stephen Heslop and Mark Robson, of course, his best friends from school. Owen Johnston too, who Mark in particular seemed to like a lot, though Sebastian tried to keep out of the way of his sour-milk breath. Nick and Grahame, his best friends from the village, who went to a different school from him because they were C of E but always seemed to get on with everybody else.

"And this year I'd like to invite Jimmy Feather."

"Oh good, I like Jimmy," his mother said.

Sebastian was uncertain how she could have formed that judgement. He could hardly remember her meeting him, perhaps a muttered hello from Jimmy at the Christmas carol service. He thought he'd better remind her who Jimmy was.

"I used to walk home with him whenever I lost my bus fare."

"I know. I think that was good for both of you."

"What do you mean?"

"Well, I think it was good for him to get to spend time with a boy like you. And I think it was good for you as well. It was certainly good exercise." She gave an odd little laugh.

Sebastian mused that she would hardly approve the friendship if she knew that Jimmy had introduced him to knocky-nine-doors and shoplifting. This was something new, to have a thought best kept secret from his mother.

"I hated walking all that way," he said sulkily.

"Well, you haven't walked for a while now, have you?" she said, standing up and beginning to clear away the tea things.

The problem of Sebastian's lost bus fares had been solved quite accidentally the previous winter by the purchase of a new pair of school trousers which happened to have a zip pocket. Sebastian had guessed that his bus fare would be safer zipped up in that pocket all day, and the losses had abruptly stopped. Around then he had started seeing much less of Jimmy, and he wanted to make up for that neglect.

The afternoon of his birthday party was another bright day, wispy clouds feathered high in a pale blue sky. Sebastian was anticipating a good party. His father had taken the day off work to help with the games, and Sebastian felt sure that whatever was in store would be thrilling, though as always it was to be a surprise.

Last year his father had bundled them all into the back of the estate car and driven them down to the river, where he had previously laid a treasure trail with blue and orange sawdust. The two trails led to secret dumps of weapons—cowboy hats and toy guns for the blue team, feathered headbands and bows and arrows for the orange—and he and his friends had spent the afternoon chasing each other over tussocks in an ecstatic game of cowboys and Indians, before squatting down on rugs to a picnic tea of bangers and beans served by his mother from the back of the estate car, renamed "the chuck wagon" for the duration of the party.

He stood in the kitchen watching through the window as his guests played in the garden, Mark, Grahame and Owen howling like monkeys as they swung across the high bars of the new climbing frame, which had been his major birthday present (though of course he acknowledged that it was for Nessa too). Stephen and Nick were kicking his new football back and forth to each other across the lawn. Everyone was enjoying himself. Yet he felt curiously fretful.

"Aren't you going out to play?" his father asked.

Sebastian shook his head. "Jimmy's not here yet."

"Are you sure he's coming?"

"I gave him the invitation. And I reminded him yesterday."

"I'm sure he'll turn up soon. You go on out and play."

"Can I see if he's coming up the hill?"

"Well, all right, if you want to."

Together Sebastian and his father went out through the front door.

Their semi-detached red brick villa stood near the top of the hill on a quiet residential road. The house had been built almost exactly a hundred years ago, his mother had told him. Its front door faced the street, and a side-door in its flank—this an unexpectedly grand touch—opened on to the short gravel drive that led from the road to the garage, then through to the back garden where his friends now jumped and whooped. A small neat garden fenced-off from their neighbours' guarded the front.

Sebastian looked down the hill, shading his eyes against the glare of the afternoon sun. There, trudging up the hill, came Jimmy, wearing his familiar green jumper.

"There he is."

Sebastian's father had seen him too, and they both watched as Jimmy slouched towards them, now level with the doctor's surgery halfway up the hill.

But something was wrong, though it was hard to define. Jimmy seemed to be walking through treacle. His feet were moving up and down, but he got no nearer.

Sebastian waved both arms. "Hi, Jimmy!"

Next to him, his father raised his arm in a friendly salute.

The movement made Sebastian glance up at his father, and he was startled to see him looking alarmed.

For Jimmy had turned smartly round and was beginning to walk back down the hill.

"Where's he going?"

"Quick, get in the car," his father said.

Sebastian and his father sprang into the front seats of the car as fast as policemen in a television programme. His father turned the ignition key and was already pulling out into the road while Sebastian was still closing the passenger door.

Jimmy trotted down the pavement, gradually picking up speed.

Sebastian's father speeded up too and their car was soon within twenty yards of him.

Jimmy glanced over his shoulder at them and broke into a run. His father accelerated again, and Jimmy veered out into the middle of the road, right in front of the car, almost filling the windscreen, running for his life, his tousled hair streaming back, the sleeves of his green jumper gripped tightly in his fists as his thin arms pumped, his rubber-soled shoes flying up behind him.

"What's he doing?" Sebastian cried out, close to tears.

His father was grim-faced. "I don't know."

Sebastian stared aghast as Jimmy galloped down the hill in frantic bone-shaking flight, taking with him all his hopes for friendship and reciprocity and kindness.

Jimmy was almost at the foot of their street now, heading for the junction with the main road, still running at full tilt.

"Good God, the traffic," his father shouted.

He braked, slamming the car to a halt, and they watched in horror as Jimmy plunged right across the main road, a passing lorry blaring its horn, brakes screaming, then he reached the far pavement and hurdled the wall, his thin shoes pounding hard across the threadbare grass towards the grimy council blocks, running, running, running away from Sebastian, running away from his friends, from his party, his house, until at last he was lost in shadow forever.

John Adams

Event Horizon

Fact: 80% of Americans do not have a passport.

Prologue

When I was a child, I spoke as a child, I understood as a child, I thought as a child. I watched Lassie, The Lone Ranger, Robin Hood[1] and so on.

When I was a man, I watched re-runs with my kids…

Somewhere

We all have our idiosyncracies. One of my own is that I have read 'A Brief History Of Time'. Twice. So I know a thing or two about singularities. Not many of us will visit a black hole but if you want an idea what it might be like, just go to the American Midwest.

The book was given by Andy B, who some years earlier had invited me into the labs of

---

1. This classic British TV series was actually written by blacklisted American writers, hounded out of the US during the McCarthy Witch Hunts. Presumably they had passports then.

the Digital Equipment Corporation, where he was working on some revolutionary software. DecTalk could translate text into speech and I was looking for a cutting edge voice-over for my new film. I thought that the system was amazing—and so later did Mr Hawking, who adopted it as his public voice to the world.

This all happened in Cambridge Massachusetts, home of DEC, spun out of MIT by its founder, Ken Olsen[2].

And it was in Cambridge that I bought a 1971 Cadillac Sedan de Ville. This was a 22ft long car made at the height of the American love affair with gasoline. A car that had electric everything, a boot to sleep 3 people and 5 cigarette lighters. It was a joke in the city. By the time I bought it, parking spaces were designed for compact cars. The Cadillac needed two of these—and two adjacent parking spaces in Boston are hard to find.

So we left Beantown, Andy B and I, to drive across the USA, for no particular reason other than there was nowhere on the East Coast to park a 1971 Cadillac.

It is possible to drive coast-to-coast in around three and a half days if you are partial to amphetamines (and many are) but we were in a more relaxed mode, Andy smoking large spliffs and talking more or less non-stop for 500 miles a day. I was quite happy about that because the American rule of radio is, *the farther West, the worse it gets*. So Andy was my entertainment.

2. Ken Olsen is also noted for his comment in 1997, "There is no reason for any individual to have a computer in his home". On listening to the constant MSN call-back noise from my daughters' bedrooms, I have to agree.

Amongst other things he told me that his father was one of the 130,000 people who worked on the Manhattan Project. Mr B didn't talk about it that much, particularly as the outcome of the venture was the death of around 220,000 Japanese citizens, in short order. But he was more forthcoming about his neighbour, the craggily handsome Leonard Bernstein, who regularly hosted risqué parties at his grand house. Leonard, who clearly had a great sense of rhythm, liked to swing both ways. Musicians. What are they like?

And so on. I have a transcript of Andy B's entire monologue from East to West but sadly cannot include it here.

Cut instead to the night time scene in Laramie, the place I wanted to visit because of my childhood experience of the TV series.

Looking now at a publicity photo of Slim Sherman and Jess Harper, I imagine Mr Bernstein may have been a fan also. Weirdly, another American musical great, Hoagy Carmichael, also starred in the show.

Ah, the black hole that is the Midwest. If you are of a certain age and it crosses your mind to visit Laramie, Fargo, Cheyenne, Four Feather Falls, or any other small American town in the title of a film, TV series or song, think again. You will surely be disappointed. All you will find there are fat people in baseball caps, outlets and malls. Whatever the American dream is, you won't find it there.

But we just had to go to Laramie. There is nothing to say about it but this:

Andy wanted to go to a saloon with swing doors but there were none, so we ended up in a bar instead. He had been smoking all day but now with the drink inside him and all that talk about Leonard, he had the urge to sing. There was a guy in the corner of the bar who looked a lot like Tom Waits, so it was the obvious cue. Andy launched into, 'There's a place for us…' in a perfect imitation of the Blue Valentine track.

The guy looked over and walked to the bar. After a few words, the barkeep handed him a well used 20 gauge and he walked over to us as Andy was hitting 'Someday… somewhere.' It was then I realised that it actually was Tom Waits—who unloaded the first barrel into the Naugahyde. Andy paused briefly, then continued, 'We'll find a new way of living…'

I had to use the bathroom, as they say. After an easy number two and a rather difficult piss, I returned to find Tom and Andy singing:

> Dear kindly Sergeant Krupke,
> You gotta understand,
> It's just our bringin' up-ke
> That gets us out of hand.

Great lyrics Mr Sondheim.

I raised a laugh, singing along in the style of Prince Charles. After a while Tom paid for the damaged upholstery and the spent shell and we parted on good terms, although he refused to sing my personal favourite, 'Gun Street Girl'. In the circumstances I didn't push it and thanked him for not killing us.

Yes, Andy B was a great mimic for sure, but not nearly as good as Stephen Hawking, who after a few drinks at a dinner party and a flick of a switch, can imitate literally anyone. He does a great George Bush apparently.

Stephen, things have moved on—it's time to change your act.

Karl McManus

Road Kill Barbecue

I've written in these pages before of the major influences in my life. Namely Charlie Dimmock. Charlie is, as I have already stated, my darling.

However, every gardener like me needs good food to fill his belly. Especially when there is decking to be laid or a water feature to dig out. For a man who is in love with the outdoors life you will not be surprised to hear that, after Charlie, my second greatest influence would have to be the great Ray Mears.

I've often thought that Ray and Charlie would make a great couple—brought together by their celebrity status and their love of the environment. If I knew either of them personally I'd be happy to make an introduction, although such an event would make me sad to see Charlie acquired by another.

ANYWAY… In Hexham we are too removed from nature. Although the folk of the North East are actually close DNA relatives of chimpanzees and the Bushmen of the Kalahari we have not lost touch with our roots. We live a life consuming too many E numbers and additives, artificial sweeteners and saturated fats and free radicals. Not enough ground nuts, berries and millet.

If we're not careful we're all going down with diverticular disease and major rectal carcinomas, as Dr Gillian McKeith has warned us on her fine programme. (I wrote to Dr McKeith asking her to come and check on my number twos but I have yet to receive a reply. I suppose she must be highly busy.)

Anyway, a couple of months ago, following Ray's advice in his programme "Extreme Survival" I went on a hunt for some proper, natural food. And I mean more than what Holland and Barret have to offer. Not just a meusli bar.

I went to Blacks in Newcastle and with my wages from my current position in the Parks department. I got a tent and a billy can, some serious camouflage Goretex and a boning knife. From the army surplus I got a cross bow and some bolts and I headed off for Slaley forest to get back to nature—as God and Ray intended.

My mission did not start well as I was stopped by the police in my Escort XR3i outside

Corbridge who confiscated my knife and cross bow and gave me a good shoeing when I made my protest.

But I was determined to show that a man from the North East can survive on bushcraft in the wild. So with no weaponry as used by our hunter/gatherer ancestors, I changed my mind and decided I would live off Road Kill for a week.

I did some research on this subject at an internet café and I discovered the following. In the USA every year:

41 million squirrels

26 million cats

22 million rats

19 million opossums

15 million raccoons

6 million dogs

350,000 deer

are wiped out as a result of road kill. That's plenty to eat. So let's BBQ!

For an appetising starter I'd recommend you find a parked car, as I did in a lay-by. Using a wire brush-a suede shoe one—remove the flies from the radiator front. Excellent and crispy-quite like the seaweed from the New Rendezvous Chinese restaurant.

What's different from America is that in Slaley the most common road kill snacks are pheasants. I found one quite soon, gutted and feathered it and buried it in a pit surrounded by hot stones I'd heated earlier. After four hours cooking I pulled it out. It was covered in hot, wet mud and leaves but was seriously tasty.

If you live in town and so have no pheasant an alternative would be well-dried and flattened squirrel which is, in my experience, quite chewy but acceptably flavoursome. You can scrape these off the tarmac with the minimum of fuss.

Ray says the supreme road kill supper is the deer. The way he takes them to pieces with his blade and bare hands is amazing. The way the guts just slop out onto the grass in a steaming heap is awesome. He should have been Hannibal Lecter!

You aren't going to find a deer that has been knocked down every day. I sat by the side of the A68 for tow days waiting for a deer to have an RTA accident but nothing happened. I didn't even see a deer, actually. Just a lot of 4x4s. And loads of rain!

With no deer available, I walked down the road and found a badger. I would not recommend badger, especially. This one was so mashed up I suspect it had been whacked by an Artic. A Christian Salveson or an Eddie Stobart probably. It had more than one set of Pirelli marks running up its back!

Anyway I stewed it over a bush fire with some wild berries and mushrooms that Ray recommended I seek out. I consumed it with a couple of lagers and the last thing I can remember is feeling pretty bad then I threw up and blacked out.

When I came round in Hexham general I'd been fed four kilos of charcoal, had my stomach pumped and my legs were quite badly burned. Apparently I had fallen into my bush fire embers. When the swelling dies down I'm having a skin graft. It's the last time I make a puffball and Yew berry sauce… I don't blame Ray, though. I just need to develop my bushcraft techniques further.

Happy Hunting!

Betsy de Lotbiniere

The Barefoot Major Domo

This is a memory I keep every time I open a *tangerine*. Using the special Opinel viniculture knife he always kept in his pocket for picnics, I thought I was cutting into a tangerine and was dismayed to find the inside a deep red. As if the fruit were inhabited by some tubercular pigeon whose heart I'd pierced. I let out a little scream. This made him laugh. "you will never forget your first blood orange!"

As often happens in beautiful places, my dreams were strong. The night before in Naples we had the fitful sleep of lovers. So I was floating the first time I swerved up and up to the top of a cliff road and saw such azure swells, the white chalkiness of the land. I am still in love with Umbrella Pines. I did not speak their language but wanted to very much. Wanted so badly to jump into their broken jawed sounds and swim in the meanings lapping all around me. I had moved to Rome in the fall. I went to Italian lessons during the day. When he was away on business feeling half a person. I would walk my dog to the middle of the Borghese Gardens and lie under the tall trees at night, dreaming of ancient Rome and how I'd be a Senator. Yes, better to be a man.

We stopped at the top of a cliff and pulled over so he could pee while I cut into and then ate the blood red orange. Sucking my fingers made no difference; they remained stained. I made Lady Macbeth jokes. We rode down to the famous port village and I tried to look. Vertigo is a feather pillow swallowed. It dances, tickles, pulls you to jump while pinning you back. Breathing up and down envisioning my spinal chord to steady myself, young enough to want to impress the new husband thinking: "I will be the fearless woman of books." But really I wanted to cry and make it stop or go more slowly but he was all about speed. He carved the road the way he did an apple, taking pleasure in his precision, skin a hair's width, keeping it all in one piece.

I had never met his great friend, Contessa G. On the drive down from Rome we had stopped in the shadow of Vesuvius and I was shown off. One delightful person after another, each so courtly and just the way you'd want Europe to present herself. I was surfaces and beautifully ironed. Kept smelling the scent of Diorissimo on my sleeve to reassure myself that I was real.

I got everyone to describe Contessa G. to me—for of course they all knew her. "She has blond hair is average height but has the strength of ten men," "she has a giant's heart", "she has slightly bucked teeth and never stops smoking", "she never wears make up but you don't notice this, because she is a bigger spirit than make up." "You have never been to her house? Oh how I envy you! I have known her since she was a *baby*… To enter that house for the first time this evening! Lucky you."

I was confused when a man opened the door because I knew that G. was meant to live alone. But the groom wasn't. "Sono Il Barbiere di villa G. al vostro sevizio!"

My groom shook hands with the burly man in a sleeveless white undershirt and dim shorts. It was explained that he was the villa's major domo. His head was round as Buddha's and he had the body of a sailor: low centre of gravity, short legs, longer barrel torso. In fact, you could say he was a bald, brown skinned, clean-shaven version of Bluto, Popeye's nemesis. He took my bags and entered the rounded door that lead to a very high ceilinged cobwebby hall with what looked like tea stained walls. An elegant rusted lantern wrought to look like vines, contained a raw bulb that made you squint to look at it, blazing the way up the impressive stairs. Walking behind Il Barbiere—for that was what everyone called this Bluto character— I noticed that his broad flat feet were bare as they slapped against the tiles. And that he had a tattoo of an *elephant* on his fury left calf muscle. Each limping step he took made the muscle ripple and gave the appearance of the elephant walking. Although our overnight bags seemed tiny in his hands—I could easily have carried mine and even offered—he wouldn't hear of it and yet never left off grumbling terribly at the weight of them.

I wasn't so much greeted as inspected by Contessa G. She was as everyone had described her but no one had spoken of her wide high cheekbones and sparkling blue eyes, so rare in Italians, that pierced me before glittering with pleasure. She kept saying I was beautiful but it was clear, as it was with everyone we met, that she wanted to speak to the groom in her own language. So I dutifully followed the Barber up to our room. His sharp grumbles diminished as he limped out of earshot though his huffing and puffing continued through the villa Once past the dining room he started mumbling repeating something with an affectionate voice. His accent was thick with a Bay of Naples accent so it took him several goes before I realized he was saying, "La Mia Madama Butterfly!" Up a sweeping back flight he began to sing snippets of an aria from that opera. He started looking back at me, his singing growing bolder as he took me down a very long and narrow corridor. He stopped when he opened the door and became more servant-like guiding me to the last room but one. He lay down my valise on a bench, the groom's on another and showed me the bathroom. Opened the double windows he invited me to inspect the spacious balcony and the sound and sight of a moonlit sea. I said thank you and how grateful I was, that I hoped his foot got better soon.

As if my kindness had opened some lid in him he turned excitedly. For such a burly man he moved swiftly grabbing my hand fiercely—before I could pull it away—to put his giant lips on my flesh saying:"La Mia Madama Butterfly!" I yelled for him to stop and might have slapped him if the voice of G. hadn't barked "Oh! Vieni qua! Barbiere!" ordering the Barbiere to return downstairs. Like a thwarted ape he shrugged and galumphed away.

I washed his beastly kiss from my hand and cheered up scrubbing the blood red orange from my fingers. I didn't want to spoil the sharply folded linen hand towel. I stood with damp arms on the balcony thinking "a Mediteranean breeze is drying me." Wild oregano and the scent of geranium floated in the salty air. The pale blue room lit by a white glass and brass lantern in the middle of the ceiling it had a sad air that evoked Visconti films. Ornate single brass beds were attached at the top and foot by two brass hands clasping each other. A matrimonial bed was still an excitement to me and I giggled sliding inside to recover from the twisting roads and all the strangeness of the Barber's passion.

The eccentric Major-domo was treated like a nasty dog. At the dining table his mistress barked her orders and would fly into a temper at the slightest misdemeanor. He, in turn, would mumble only to be showered with a string of expletives. His wife was in the kitchen the next morning, a tall, slim but sturdily boned woman wearing a scoop necked dress, also in bare feet. With a crown of salt and pepper curls on top of shining dark eyes, she would have looked like a *gypsy queen* had she kept her mouth shut. For she had barely five teeth in her head and spoke in the tuneless way of the stone deaf even though she herself was not hard of hearing. It did not stop her from making a meandering moaning sound when she worked.

Looking back on it now a great deal of the ensuing trouble could be blamed on my foreign-ness. While the Contessa had a dazzling wit and masterful story-telling technique as well as the great hostess's knack of pulling the best out of her guests, releasing a coaxing shower of questioning on whoever was at her table, her behavior as an employer would not have been tolerated in America. The Barbiere's real name was Francesco which made me laugh because his wife's name was Francesca. I started calling him Francesco and because I had not yet mastered the correct usage for the polite verb form and the informal verb forms, I stuck with the formal.

We went to visit the Contessa at her seaside villa as often as we could and in the winter months it was always the greatest honour and pleasure to be in her company in Rome. When it came time for us to move to London I begged my husband to let us summer a little in one of the Contessa's little cottages. As it turned out, my beloved could not join me for a fortnight so I was left in the dwindling last days of July alone.

My skin is pale and delectable to mosquitoes. There was only one pathway up from the cottages and only one road down to the shops in the village. So every time I went to the one grocery shop I was forced to pass the Barbiere's tiny little shop beneath the villa that the family let him have. He stopped me on my way down when he saw the red welts on my arms. Said the cure for the mosquitoes was a basil bush. He kept bugging me about getting one, saying, "I will give you some basil and why don't you come in and see my *monkey*… La Mia Madama Butterfly." The way he said it made me think perhaps it was a euphemism. So each time I passed—without a basil bush—I had to pretend I had a pressing engagement until one day on my way out, he was standing outside his shop with his wife. I returned with my bag filled with mozarella di buffala, olive oil, tomatoes, coffee, milk and in my other hand I proudly marched past the local couple with a small basil plant in a green plastic pot.

Francesca stood in her toothless, barefoot glory, with her arms crossed, nodding her head as she watched him summon me. Only her presence made me feel safe enough to go in. The shop's arched ceiling was painted white, about the size of a walk-in closet, the like of which I was not to see again until visiting Delhi. The stuccoed walls were covered in a jungle of plants. Sure enough I met the jolly little black and white creature who he called Zuniga and kept on a long string attached from the door of his cage in the corner to his little ankle. Since his wife was there I even risked getting into his barber's chair as it was really the only way three people could fit. The old chrome and black leather seat was angled in such a way that one mirror reflected off another and another until you had an excellent view of the sea. When the *monkey* landed on my lap and lifted up my skirt I shrieked and he roared with laughter. His wife hit him on the arm for that and told me the basil plant I had in my hand was way too little to be of any use against mosquitoes.

August came the next day and took away the last remaining breath of air. Heat so bad it was like breathing hot cotton. Every step was arduous and made sweat pour down and clothing stick. The only thing for it was to keep the shutters closed and stay indoors where the thick stone walls and marble floors retained a memory of cool. Wait it out until the sun went down. In the evening there was a carnival air in the bars as although getting drunk made you sweat more, it brought dark humour, forgetfulness and at least a few blessed hours of oblivion through sleep. The whole village seemed to be on a bender. In the heat the next day, cocktail flus made everyone ill humored. I stayed indoors except to go out for supplies. I could hear people bickering in the house next door and up on the street above my little cottage.

It was my habit to rise early, walk down to the port for a swim before the beach got too hot and return for breakfast. Then settle down to a stint of writing on a table beneath a canopy of violent magenta bougainvillea. This day it was too hot to think and even reading was a trouble. I struggled through the morning, made a salad for lunch then in a fit of cabin fever hit upon the idea of filling the bath with cold water and adding two measly ice trays full of ice. But when I stood up it felt as if my hair and body dried instantly. The thought of getting dressed again seemed unbearable. I resorted to dampening my sheets, shutting the shutters, putting on some Debussy, and lay down for a luxurious siesta.

Just as I had reached a dream there was a loud knock on the shutters and the sound of someone trying to shove their way in. I screamed and then heard the awful words, "La Mia Madama Butterfly. Sono il Barbiere. Sono arrivato con una pianta di basilico." The Barbiere had decided to deliver some basil. I said, thank you very much but that I was having a siesta and could he please leave his basil on the terrace. He said he wanted to show it to me. I said that wasn't necessary as I already had a basil plant and knew what it looked like. He said mine was useless and that he wanted to show me his. I said I would see it later. He said he wanted to water my plants. I said I'd already done so. Then silence. Then I heard the snaking of my hose and trickling of water and knew he was quenching the thirst of the geraniums on the terrace. I went back to dozing.

I felt the darkness of his presence in the room even before he spoke, and screamed. He'd let himself in via the kitchen, had crossed through the sitting room and was standing in the doorway. I shrieked for him to leave. He spoke in his baritone. "Solo un oretta" he was asking for a "little hour", hushing me as if I were unruly livestock. There was another door to the bathroom. Luckily he was carrying a giant basil bush and was intent upon setting it down on a table. I raced for the bathroom door and my clothes but he was too quick, pushed it shut before I got there. I ducked behind him, twisting the damp sheet around me as I ran. I didn't have any more of a plan but to get outside where if I screamed I'd have a better chance of being heard. I was calling out, "leave me alone!" and he kept entreating, "solo un oretta!" galumphing after me, using his advantage of width and brawn as much as he could to bar my way, attempting to corner me. I looked at all the houses of my neighbours and realized they were all either at the beach or on a boat trying to catch a stray breeze.

I grabbed the one good knife in the kitchen but he quickly removed it from me as I had to use my other hand to keep myself covered by the sheet. By the third circling of the house a little voice inside me calmed me down with these words: "he's bigger than you but you're smarter, start talking and using your brain."

My arguments were these: "I am a married woman and my husband is due to arrive any minute" (but the Barbiere knew as well as I did he wasn't coming for another three days). "Solo un oretta!" he said, throwing my kitchen knife over the parapet into the garden below.

"You will go to hell for cheating on your wife." Surprised when he laughed and repeated his refrain. I was heading for the gate onto the semi-private footpath that led to the road above. I backed into a wrought iron chair and when I turned to see where I was going, he leapt behind me. His arms were wide and when I got to the kitchen door I realized he'd locked it. "I'll tell the Contessa." His intent did not even register this threat. There seemed no escape. He lunged towards me and I kicked him in the shin, which caused my bare foot a great deal more pain than it did his shin. His voice was calm and sweet, as if he knew I'd concede, "solo un oretta".

"I will tell your wife!" and at last the spark of hunger went out of his big dark eyes. But he kept coming towards me. Then I took aim and kicked him in the nuts. It was a strange feeling. Like kicking a cushion between two tree trunks. "I will tell your wife and the Contessa and my husband." He held his crotch but only in a symbolic way. "Oh La Mia Madama Butterfly!" he said, quite deflated, finally awake to the risk he'd taken.

Then I had the upper hand and didn't stop shouting "get out! I'll tell them all if you don't. Leave now and never return or I'll tell your wife first, then my husband and he'll have words with the Contessa." At last he started to move away from me. I kicked him in the ass as soon as his back was turned and he left in his gorilla trot.

I hid out in the cottage for the next three days. It was more expensive to ring up and have the groceries delivered but it was worth it. Meant I had to explain to the husband. When he arrived the heat wave had been dispelled. The locals all knew it was usual for the wind to pick up after the 15th and suddenly there was life in the village. That he laughed when I told him the story brought an outburst of tears. I begged him not to tell the Contessa or confront the Barbiere, that I had handled the situation. He swore he would keep his silence.

Three days later I was taking a coffee at the Bar Barto, just outside Contessa G.'s villa. There was a sudden explosion of abuse on the terrace of the villa and from the street I could see the gorilla trot of the Barbiere followed by the blonde head of the Contessa. She was calling him a pig and kicking him. In an instant I knew she was talking about me. Worse was his reaction: "you are just jealous you did not get her alone yourself!" so it had not been my imagination that she had been staring at me. After that the story spread like wildfire. Then everywhere I went in the village I could hear giggles and the horrid murmur of that wretched refrain: "solo un oretta"! For it turned out that the phrase was not a part of modern Italian parlance.

I was furious with the husband who seemed overly fond of being at the center of the drama. He said I was being too sensitive, that it would all blow over. But time has woven a different tapestry than one might have thought. The *monkey*, the Barbiere Francesco and his wife, Francesca were both dead ten years later. The poor romantic barber had contracted diabetes in later life. Just as they were going to amputate his left foot he was found in his barber's chair dead of an overdose of very expensive chocolates. The husband and I divorced.

In a kind letter from the Contessa, she said she was sorry our marriage hadn't lasted. But she said the spirit of the Barbiere and me that summer still haunted her. She is in the property development business. She was overseeing the construction of an hotel in Florence. Standing with her architect one day at the base of her site they waiting for the foreman to sign off on something. They called up to him and he called back "Oh! Solo un oretta! La Mia Madama

Butterfly!" And she realized she'd told the story to the architect who'd told it to the foreman who must have told it to all the men on the sight because they were suddenly all folded over in peals of laughter.

Geoffrey Orde

North by North-East

When I was young, a train journey was an adventure. Nose pressed against a sooty window, I would look out into the world, daydreaming cops, robbers and crashes, seldom taking notice of other passengers, unless they annoyed me. Rather like the woman in an airline seat who, many years later, kicked me two or three times on a train to Newcastle. I smiled weakly, as one does, and grunted "No problem" on each occasion. We were approaching York and she couldn't get her case from the rack above her head. As I helped her with her bags, I looked at her. She was strikingly attractive, about fifty and dressed in well-made, well-fitting clothes. She smiled at me and I caught a trace of her scent as she sprayed her wrist. It was one of the most striking and special I know: The Habbinaya, from where the Tigris joins the Euphrates in Iraq.

"You're wearing the most wonderful perfume, The Habbinaya, isn't it?"

"Thank you," she replied with a smile, "Not many people know it, it's extremely rare…"

The train was slowing as it approached York. She looked at me without blinking.

"You know, I'm not in a great hurry and I know a wonderful little Italian restaurant here. Will you join me? I hate eating alone,"

"I'm not rushing anywhere either," I said, grabbing my case.

Emilio's was indeed wonderful and so was she. After a couple of bottles of a particularly decent Chianti, I realised we'd hardly had time to eat, we were talking so much. Our knees touched, our hands joined, rational thought had stayed on the train.

Her flat was in the Wall of York. It was elegant, comfortable and feminine. The front door clunked shut with a reassuring thud. We tumbled into each other's arms and stayed there for some time. I was in no hurry to change anything apart from position from time to time, and neither was she.

We're approaching York. The tannoy drones on incomprehensibly. I pull my face away from the window, the daydream is over. The lady opposite asks me to help with her case from the overhead rack, "Excuse me," I say "you're wearing the most wonderful perfume, is it er… Habbinaya by any chance?"

Karl Macmanus

Black, Wet Night

Black night is not right,
I don't feel so bright,
I don't care to sit tight.
Maybe I'll find on the way down the line
That I'm free, free to be me.
Black Night is a long way from home.
I don't need a dark tree,
I don't want a rough sea,
I can't feel, I can't see.
Maybe I'll find on the way down the line
That I'm free, free to be me.
Black night is a long way from home.
(Gillan, Blackmore, Glover, Lord, Paice)

I want to write and talk with you about a problem that effects millions across the nation. That problem is nocturnal enuresis. To give it it's proper medicinal name.

I wet the bed. So this is a request for a better public understanding of a condition that I've suffered from for too long. I've suffered from it from a very early age—from when I was born, actually. But I think that my mum first realised there was a problem when I was about fourteen years old. As I was an only child she didn't realise that by this age being dry at night was usual. By the time I had –I've worked out—gone through about 11,672 nappies. That's a lot of landfill which I know, as a man of nature, is not good for the environment, even if they are made of non-chlorinated wood pulp. I had to do something.

Mum took me to the doctor and he recommended that I didn't have anything to drink after lunchtime each day. That wasn't easy, especially with these long hot Summers we have up here in the North East. During one July day I was admitted to hospital with severe dehydration. It didn't work and my rubber sheet on the mattress had to stay.

The next thing the doctors tried was a Night Alarm. This machine is plugged into the socket and wired up to your pads when you go to bed and if the extremely sensitive sensors are able to detect fluid of any sort in the night an alarm goes off. This wakes you up and reminds you to go to the toilet in the toilet. Instead of in your bed. And what a noise. It sounded just like the alarm on my first Astra GTE.

Anyway it worked a few times before I had a serious problem with the apparatus. It was one night when I was about sixteen. I went to bed as usual with everything switched on. Maybe I had too many lagers, I don't know. I'm not sure what happened exactly—maybe a short circuit or a power surge or something. Maybe I had the sensitivity levels adjusted too high. But at around 2.45 AM when I had the attack of enuresis my whole body plus the bed started shaking and then I got the full 240 volts through my privates! You can laugh, readers but at the same time I wasn't amused at all. I don't mind telling you it was a bit of a shock quite literally!!

My enuresis has not helped my love life. In my late teenage years after a lot of searching in Hexham and even the back streets of Consett I met Karen who is a beautiful beautician as we queued together for some takeaway at the New Rendezvous on the Darras Hall Estate. We started going out and you should see the job she did on my toenails! Things went well and, although I will ever hold a candle for Charlie Dimmock who, as readers know, is my darling, I decided it was time to consummate my love for Karen. The first obstacle I had to overcome when getting Karen into my bedroom was explaining my Star Chart on the wall. I get a star for every dry night. (I told her it was an old school art project.)

I don't want to go into any intimate detail of our love-making that night but I'm sure Karen enjoyed it a lot.

We went to sleep but in the middle of the night I woke up because Karen was screaming. I didn't know what was going on—maybe there was an intruder in the room. I leapt from my bed to grab my Ray Mears Adventure knife which I always keep handy. Just in case. Hexham can be a dangerous place in these violent times.

There wasn't any intruder. Unfortunately. Far worse. I had forgotten to turn the machine on and you can guess what happened.

When I told the doctor what had occurred he said "I wonder if she was worried you'd never reach Mount Ararat." I'm not sure what he meant by that.*

Karen and I didn't see much of each other after that night.

I often suffer relapses of my problem during times when my self-esteem is low. After my episode when I tried to Road Kill BBQ and ended up in casualty with burns after I fell in the fire I wet the bed several times on the ward at Hexham General. The nurses were so cross I got catheterized. I did not feel this was a very sensitive response to a very real problem. One day I will find someone who really understands.

---

*Mount Ararat was where Noah's Ark landed after the waters of the Great Flood receded. I feel this shows remarkable insensitivity towards Karl and his condition but knowing the GP in question, I cannot say I am surprised. (ed)

Delaval Hastings

Armchair Theatre

When I was seven years old and we lived at Thornage Grange, I found a place that I liked beneath the leather armchair my father used.

From its homely, dilapidated look, I knew his seat had been around for longer than I had. The whole house had a well-worn appearance, and that is not something I have normally associated with my parents, not anyway before they became well-worn themselves. Because they took pride in their homes, my mother in particular.

Perhaps its neglect stemmed from it being an in-between house, from which my father could keep an eye on what was to become our real home: a large farmhouse which they were in the process of doing up and extending and where neither he nor my mother had overlooked any detail or angle.

This camp, as we thought of it, was allowed to exist in happy disarrangement. To us it had a breezy appeal. There were square-patterned rush mats downstairs but few carpets. Upstairs, there were rugs, those little stripey ones people put beside their beds for their feet to rest on before they get into their slippers.

The edges of my bedroom had white-painted edges. These made a kind of frame or boundary around the middle where there was nothing, paint or otherwise, to cover the pine floorboards where my bed sat.

People tended to linger by the door, deterred by that white line and reluctant to advance, as if the room were a cordoned-off exhibit. Once or twice I woke up imagining that I might be sinking though the floor and that I would be safe if I could reach the solid ground where the whitened border was. These waking dreams scared the life out of me and were related perhaps to the impermanence of our situation. I think they also showed a desire for freedom and escape, even at that age, despite there being few blights on my happiness.

At around the same time, I discovered a form of truancy at the local school, although, in the strictest sense, I was never truly absent from Form 5's frowsty classroom.

It was more of a disappearing act, designed to grab the attention of a group of children I had not grown up with. I would vanish into the corner cupboard at the back of the class, there to wait out the lesson, a few yards away from our teacher, the saintly Mrs Ryder, who, in her tweed jackets and with her love of cricket, maintained an unfathomable fondness for me.

I had pictured my hiding as a show-stopping piece of daring but it turned out otherwise. My enjoyment was undermined by long spells of boredom as well as unbearable moments of anxiety. The stunt rendered meaningless by the frankly bewildered looks of my classmates. The only pleasure was in getting out undetected. In contrast, to a daydreamer, the underside of my father's chair provided an escape in itself.

As a place it was no more conducive to flights of fancy than gazing into a fire or staring dreamily out of a window for minutes on end. But, because it was a find that I had made on my own and one I managed to keep to myself for quite a while, it had a special significance.

With its sagging hessian roof and dusty floor, dry odour and corners terminating in four metal castors, it was a comfortably contained world into which I peered like a fish, mind in neutral, in those moments of childhood shutdown, when whatever drives the body seems to have been exhausted.

The chair's low-slung arch became a kind of theatre for an imagination fed on characters from comics, books, and just about anything that had ever happened to it. The players wandered onto this stage with no conscious effort on my part. Roger Bannister ran ever quicker, achieving staggering times, three minutes thirty, three minutes fifteen for the mile. Imperilled Londoners in a runaway tube-train were snatched to safety by Mr Veltman, our neighbour: part man, part eagle. I whiled happy times away there with Deborah Kerr. She glided around the house, in a bikini normally, and I spent my time hunting jaguar.

Whatever dramas were played out under that leather chair were in the miniaturist's scale, and the most barbarous of these were made the more manageable for that. When I was not imagining anything, which was a lot of the time, I drifted, thinking of nothing and doing less.

Just before Christmas a spring poked through the roof, altering the landscape. I thought it gave added interest, if that were possible. It promised a higher dimension from which gods might descend. The spring gave me what turned out to be a bad idea, but which, unsurprisingly, seemed to me to be a stroke of near-genius.

I managed to keep it to myself for four whole months before it popped out. Throughout my childhood, I was doomed to try and win my sister's approval; she was older, bigger, and stronger than me and her idea of fun was to make me suffer. I tried almost anything to make her like me but never hit my target. Except that day, when I told her about the spring and the joke that I wanted to play with it. For an hour or two afterwards, I felt the heady elatedness of her seeing me in a different light, no longer the snivelling little brother, but an accomplice in mischief. My idea was to connect a twelve-volt battery to that spring so that when my father was at his most relaxed, sitting down with a whisky and the evening paper, maybe lighting a cigarette and anticipating his supper, I would give him an electric shock.

Unfortunately, the blue rectangular battery would not fit under the chair, so we took the vase from the table and put it behind that. Even to our undomesticated, none-too-picky eyes, a flower vase on the floor was incongruous. We put a magazine over the battery and hoped that my father would not see it.

'I want to see it work.' Said Sophia, predictably enough. 'Sit on it.'

'Sit on it yourself.'

I was normally gullible, obedient or fearful enough to follow these sorts of instruction. But we were talking about my idea, and that made me reluctant to roll over. Persistent as ever, Sophia pushed on.

'What's the matter? Scared? Frightened of a battery?' She said, and it's clear that my choice boils down to this: get a shock or have me call you a coward. Mercy is a laboratory concept to Sophia.

'Okay, then.' I said, trying for a debonair approach. 'If you want me to, Sophia, but the battery won't work afterwards… He probably wouldn't even feel it.' I could see doubt in her punchy demeanour, despite the jut of her jaw, a trace of uncertainty that made her heavy-browed, and a little stupid-looking. 'It'll drain it flat. Use up all its power. Of course if you still want me to, just to prove I'm not scared….' It sounded semi-plausible, even to me.

Sophia, for whom anything technical was uncertain ground, turned away, looking towards the window.

I sensed her disappointment, a deflation about her. When she spoke again she had a conciliatory tone, friendly even, my co-conspirator once more, pugnacity in retreat.

'Well, I suppose we'd better disconnect it then, if that's the case. We want to give him a real jolt don't we?'

With so much to look forward to in the evening and nothing much before, the afternoon was slow work. Only visits to the battery to see if it was still there, the magazine in place, lifted the ennui. Then there was more waiting when my father finally arrived. For the nightly ritual of ablutions to be over, the shave, the putting on of the fresh shirt, the unhurried descent down the stairs, until at last he appeared, spruced up and emitting the whiff of freshly soaped skin, in the sitting-room.

He slumped down, at the end of an effortful day, closed his eyes, drew in and then exhaled a long breath. Here it was, the moment we had both been expecting, and soon, I was sure, he would be jumping out of his chair. But, to my dismay nothing happened: no leap skywards, no stung expression, no spilt drink, nothing. We watched his hand go to the base of his spine, and give it a scratch, and I took heart, thinking that somehow my trick must be working, but after that the only movement that either hand made was to turn the pages of his newspaper. That was it, nothing, nothing that is but for the slowly rising look of contempt on my sister's face.

That was Sophia for you, a friend one minute, an enemy for the rest of your life. Next day, with appropriate scorn, she passed the details of my brainwave up the family food chain to my brother, hoping, no doubt, that it would be one of those titbits, evidence of unbeatable stupidity, that they could taunt me with for months. But he did not find me that stupid. In fact, the only shortcoming of my plan, as far as he could see, was not in the thinking, but in the power source.

'Too puny. A twelve volt battery? You need a lot more that that.' Not even a car battery had enough of a charge, in his opinion, to create the kind of spectacle we wanted. He left his bedroom, where we he had been sitting among his slowly-built collection of dirty clothes, records, and stained mugs and headed downstairs. We caught up with him raiding the family's meagre toolkit. Then, neck bowed with an air of determination, he marched into the sitting room with pliers and a screw driver, where he set about dismantling the lamp, removing the bulb, unscrewing the top, and then the wires. Ignoring our questions, a crevice of concentration across the top of his nose, he tipped the chair on its back, wound the threads of shiny electrical wire around the spring, pinched them tight with the pliers and lay the chair back down on its feet. He fed the flex out towards the socket.

'That's what you need.' He said. 'Plug it in and flick the switch.'

What?' This was all happening too quickly. I thought I knew what was going on but at the same time I could not believe he was serious. I felt remorse. The person who had least wanted this space threatened, myself, the one who had set all of it in motion, had only himself to blame.

'Won't that…? I mean…'

'Kill him? I should think so. What do you think? An electric chair. Look.'

That's how I lost the chair: an idea that I should have let blow over did for that lovely old seat. I should have kept it to myself and it would not have ended as it did, with all the fuses in the house blown, the chair destroyed, the horsehair singed, the leather charred and the smell of acrid plastic lingering in the sitting room for weeks; with my mother making excuses to my father, suspecting us but unable to prove anything, everyone denying all knowledge, and the chair hastily removed to the garden, and from there to I don't know where.

Jamie Warde-Aldam

Chanel No.5

I hate tests, don't you? Never been any good at them. Maybe they'd be less humiliating if you were given more time. Then again, the stress of having to live with a difficult question skulking in your head for days would be unendurable, for me at least. It would ruin everything else I tried to do. Tests just do my head in.

Some people are really good at them, though. During the 1960s and 70s, a London advertising agency gave prospective copywriters a test to gauge their creative thinking. One question was 'How would you sell toast to a Martian?' To which one put-on-the-spot genius answered, "OOObaglobzidorgakbeeezulskobbleebloptwinkerbleepsko-baxz!" How fantastically, irritatingly clever. I wonder what he's doing now?

Then there's the spy test. It's supposed to establish the resourcefulness of a would-be

MI5-er to a sudden change in situation. It's very 1930s and it goes like this.

Your mistress is offended by a casual remark you make. In the ensuing row, she empties the contents of an enormous bottle of Chanel No. 5 over you. You stumble out of her flat reeking of the scent, which will cling to you for three days at the very least. How do you explain this away to your wife?

After a few seconds of total panic, I told the guy who asked me that I'd phone my wife and explain that I was going to be away on a spy selection course for the next few days and would she please not mention it to anyone.

Then, privately, I thought I'd patch it up with my mistress and live at her place near Marble Arch until I began to smell like me, not her. Lots of long baths, her saying how sorry she was, scrambled eggs, smoked salmon; a pretty good outcome really.

Ah, shit, hold on. I don't have a mistress, *she was in the spy test*, *she's not fucking real*. Get a grip Willis! But I was there, being vetted for MI5 surely, I could just feel it.

That's how these people recruit isn't it? At parties and so on. All that stuff about going through normal bureaucratic channels is just such obvious PC bollocks.

No, I think I acquitted myself well in that little encounter. Although not *that* well, as it turns out. A day or so later, I (ho-hum) bumped into Andrew, the guy who asked me the question, and he told me that the proper answer was to go home and tell one's wife exactly what had happened. She would find the story so incredible, she'd just laugh, he said.

We're having a drink next Friday. I know he's interested, still testing me here and there, keeping an eye on my movements. To think that I'm being considered for spy material… I feel a quietly confident thrill in my stomach.

About forty-five minutes ago, I walked into Selfridges perfumery department, bought two large bottles of Chanel No.5, went to the bins at the back of Davies Street and emptied them over myself. It felt lovely and cold; it's quite a hot day today. Then I got on the tube, had a bit of bother with some youths who taunted me on the Northern Line, mopped up my bleeding lip with a tissue and I'm just walking up to our front door.

Wish me luck!

Dudley's Regret

In the first months after Joanna left, Dudley kept his own company. The silence of the house was something he needed. it bolstered his pretence that she was still there, in one of her extended, mute sulks. Switching on the wireless was like breaking a spell. Even the rustle of a newspaper was sacrilege to the quiet he cultivated.

Mrs Abingdon, the cleaner, had continued to come in two mornings a week and, he reflected, did her level Christian best for him. But his leaden glooms and irritable shushings defeated her generous nature and she'd given in her notice.

Now of course it was different. 18 Basset Grove was like a TV stage set for a bachelor sitcom.

A fridge full of gin, tonic, olives and white wine, Mozart on the music centre and, this

morning, the heart-quickening snap of elastic on bare thigh, as Julie got herself ready for
a lunchtime shift at the Black Horse.

They'd met shortly after he'd decided to smoke himself to death. A neat way to avoid the stigma of suicide, he thought: slow and, he'd read, relatively painless. It wouldn't take long at his age. He'd left the house for the first time in months and walked nervously towards the pub over the damp common. It was midday and their eyes locked before either had time to speak. Dudley forgot about change for the cigarette machine and asked for a gin and tonic. He was
a well-kept sixty-five year old with a slightly ruffled look and nicely tailored trousers.

She had chestnut hair, green eyes and a smoky laugh which suggested everything unsuitable you'd care to imagine.

Twice married, she'd recently finished with the last in a longish line of sulky young men from the local cricket team. She informed Dudley that she was looking for someone she couldn't steal sweets from. He'd bought her a bag of gobstoppers and a bottle of Bailey's that afternoon. Their relationship was founded on a mutual sigh of relief that the world had suddenly become less complicated.

Life revolved around the Dirty Donkey as the regulars called the place. Tarquin, the landlord, had cleverly targeted the ageing Gin n' Jag set and there wasn't a lunchtime where retired doctors, bank managers and stockbrokers weren't queuing for gastro-pub fare. Younger drinkers usually took one look at the wrinkled contents of the saloon bar and fled. There was something almost shocking about witnessing senior citizens in such glowing health: talking, flirting like teenagers and downing expensive-looking drinks as if there was no tomorrow.

The Black Horse was a club in essence, much like the milk bars Dudley had hung about in as a teenager, and the pub back rooms where he'd skulked in his undergraduate years. There was no need for a door policy: sheer terror kept everyone else away. Subscriptions were rolled into Tarquin's stealthy and exorbitant mark-ups and the dress code was a particular English smart/casual which spelt money and little else.

And so, Dudley was content to all outward appearances. He didn't think about Joanna very much. And when, occasionally, his expression became melancholy and Julie asked tenderly if he was thinking about "her", he'd change the subject. She wouldn't have understood the other void in his life, where his loss, although minor in comparison, was perpetual. Twenty-five years ago, in one of his spurious financial spring cleans, he'd thought he could dispense with an amateur publication called The Hotspur and had let his patronage slip. Little had he anticipated the longueurs, dull conversations and the sheer predictability of his resultant, corporately spoon-fed existence. No other periodical or activity had ever succeeded in replacing that small but significant ray of sunlight for him.

Into every life a little rain must fall, he thought with an overused sigh.

But, deep down, he knew it wasn't good enough.

He reached for his cheque book.

Thank you for reading this. If you'd like to remain or indeed become a Hotspur patron and help the magazine to continue, cheques (£25 for four issues) can be made out to Healey PCC c/o JWA, Healey, Riding Mill, Northumberland, NE44 6BH

The Contributors

Betsy de Lotbiniere runs Mesoteric, a monthly gathering of artists, musicians, writers, film-makers and appreciative audiences. She lives in Holland Park.

Jamie Warde-Aldam edits The Hotspur and is from Healey.

Karl McManus, a native of Hexham, Northumberland, is eighteen years old and currently employed by the Parks Department.

Norman Baker used to write for the New Musical Express. His current whereabouts are unknown.

Adam Douglas is an antiquarian book dealer and lives in Clapham.

Delaval Hastings keeps to himself in Norfolk.

John Adams is a film-maker and lives in Heaton.

Geoffrey Orde used to fly Meteor jets and is based in Riding Mill.

The Hotspur

The Hotspur is the parish magazine of St John's, Healey, in south Northumberland. It appears as many as four times a year. Every issue has a different theme and contains a free print by a first-rate poet or artist.

Although it has no cover price and isn't made for profit, the magazine is fortunate to have a readership outside the parish. These terrific people pay twenty-five pounds for four issues and are our patrons. They enjoy special limited editions and, occasionally, get their hands on the much-coveted Hotspur t-shirt, which we screen-print from time to time.

With its tiny circulation the magazine needs all the help it can get. Buying this anthology will help secure it a little more independence and a future.

If you'd like to sample the magazine in pdf form, please email thehotspur@googlemail.com and I'll be delighted to send one to you. It's obviously not the same as the real thing but it'll give you an idea of whether you'll enjoy it or not.

If, after that, you do wish to become a patron and receive the magazine, please turn to the story Dudley's Regret for more details.

Thank you.

Jamie Warde-Aldam, editor, *The Hotspur*.

Edited by Jamie Warde-Aldam, 2009.

ISBN 978–0–906630–40–2

Typeset by Colin Sackett
Produced by Coracle for The Hotspur
Printed in China

The Hotspur, Healey, Riding Mill, Northumberland, NE44 6BH
thehotspur@googlemail.com